THE ATOMIC DEBATES

Sir Benjamin Collins Brodie

(From a photograph taken *c.* 1875)

THE
ATOMIC DEBATES

Brodie and the Rejection
of the Atomic Theory

THREE STUDIES

Edited by

W. H. BROCK

Lecturer in the History of Science
in the University of Leicester

LEICESTER UNIVERSITY PRESS

1967

Printed in Great Britain
by T. & A. Constable Limited for
Leicester University Press

CONTENTS

v

FOREWORD

IN his Presidential Address to the British Association for the Advancement of Science in 1901, the physicist A. W. Rücker suggested that the three great theoretical problems of nineteenth-century science, which were still unresolved, had been the mechanical nature of heat, the existence of an ether, and the existence of atoms. Within a decade of his remarks, however, the work of Perrin, Einstein, Rutherford and von Laue had made it no longer practicable to doubt the validity of an atomic-molecular model. Meanwhile, through the historical writings of Henry Roscoe, Pattison Muir, von Meyer, and many others, a tradition grew up that the atomic-molecular theory had been one of the great theoretical successes of nineteenth-century physics and chemistry. However, just as recent research by historians of chemistry suggests that John Dalton was not the *conscious* inventor of the chemical atomic theory, the other traditional view that Dalton immediately and successfully convinced chemists of the truth and power of atomism has proved far too simple.

In the past historians have paid a good deal of attention to the development of the atomic-molecular theory, with an emphasis on the problems of nomenclature, the interpretation of gravimetric and volumetric laws of combination and the determination of suitable atomic weights. All of these studies have been invaluable; but apart from the pioneering effort of Joshua C. Gregory in his *A Short History of Atomism* (London, 1931), little research has been done on nineteenth-century scepticism towards atomism, or on the frequent outright rejection of Dalton's atomic theory. The present group of studies seeks to examine some of the reasons for this scepticism, and to provide a detailed account of one chemist's serious alternative to atomism. The historical background to the rejection of the atomic theory by chemists is given in the first study. The two other essays provide a full analysis of Sir Benjamin Brodie's 'Calculus of Chemical

vii

Operations,' together with the publication for the first time of an important selection from his correspondence on this subject. A short Appendix considers the possible influence of Comte's Positivism on chemists' rejection of atoms.

The idea for this book came from Mr Rom Harré who, on another occasion, had been the intellectual catalyst behind the publication by Dr David Knight and myself of an article on the mid-century debates among chemists over atomism. One of Harré's pupils, Mr Duncan Dallas, had prepared a very thorough analysis of Brodie's Calculus; and later, in 1964, when the Library of the University of Leicester acquired some of Brodie's scientific correspondence, Harré suggested that the publication under one cover of the results of the work of Knight, Dallas and myself might provide a useful and interesting case history of atomic scepticism. All errors, needless to say, are entirely those of the contributors.

While it is to be expected that these studies will be of primary use to historians of science and to undergraduates reading courses in this discipline, it is hoped that as a case history of a form of *operationalism* which preceded and anticipated Bridgman's use of the term by some sixty years, they will also interest the philosopher. In addition, we believe that much of our material will intrigue and stimulate the professional chemist and mathematician, and the teacher of these two subjects.

Many of our debts to various individuals are recorded elsewhere in the book. Here our acknowledgements are accorded to the editors of *Isis* and *Studies in Romanticism* for their permission to draw on two articles that were first published in their journals; namely, W. H. Brock and D. M. Knight, 'The Atomic Debates,' *Isis*, *56*, 5-25, 1965, and D. M. Knight, 'The Atomic Theory and the Elements,' *Studies in Romanticism*, *5*, 185-207, 1966. Permission to reproduce passages from P. W. Bridgman, *Logic of Modern Physics* (London, 1960), is gratefully accorded to The Macmillan Company, New York, who hold the copyright. The Council of the Royal Society granted leave for the transcription of a plate from one of Brodie's papers published in the Society's *Philosophical Transactions*. My thanks are due to the Librarian of the Royal Society, Mr I. Kaye, who readily placed the Herschel archives at my disposal and answered my queries. Mr F. R. Maddison, Curator of the Museum of History of Science at Oxford, allowed two of us to thoroughly explore the Brodie papers in his care, and kindly gave permission for the publication of three letters. It is a pleasure to thank the Misses P. M. and O. M. Brodie for their generous permission to reproduce the hitherto unpublished photograph of their grandfather which is in their possession. Finally, I am personally indebted to D. M. Knight for the magnanimous way in which he allowed yet another of his essays on the atomic theory to be 'drawn and quartered' by me and its conclusions fused into the joint essay which is here published. To Professor Simmons I owe much encouragement; and to Mr B. J. Roud, Secretary to the Board of the Leicester University Press, I owe an editor's gratitude for the careful way he handled a complicated manuscript.

Leicester, August 1966   W. H. BROCK

I

The Atomic Debates

by

W. H. BROCK and D. M. KNIGHT

IT has been suggested that nobody doubted the existence of God until the Boyle Lecturers tried to prove it. The same kind of remark could be made about atoms; few seem to have doubted that matter was composed of atoms of some sort until Dalton's theory came out in the early years of the nineteenth century. Among chemists a large number remained frankly sceptical about atoms until the conversion of Wilhelm Ostwald in the early years of the present century. We are therefore faced with a whole century of scepticism in which the opponents of atomism attacked on at least three fronts.

It was widely believed that the history of chemistry would parallel that of astronomy, and that mathematical laws would replace causal explanations. Others believed that unobservable entities should be rigorously excluded from the science. There was also a widespread reluctance to believe that there could be very many different kinds of ultimate elementary materials. The atomic theory of Dalton did not seem to those who thought in these ways a satisfactory step in the right direction.

It appears that chemistry in England after Humphry Davy and William Wollaston had ceased to do important work passed through a pusillanimous period of consolidation. The glamour with which Davy had invested the science did not survive him, and chemistry became a by-word for its plodding methods.[1] John Herschel hoped that the experimental phase in chemistry would be succeeded by a period in which it would become a deductive, mathematical science.[2] The laws of chemistry had been arrived at by pure enumerative induction; therefore they yielded no important discoveries. Chemical theories, for the same reason, were 'for the most part of that generally intelligible and readily applicable kind, which demand no intense concentration of thought, and lead to no profound mathematical researches.' Because of the complexity of the science: 'the *axioms* of chemistry, the true handles of deductive reasoning . . . [are] still unknown, and, perhaps, likely long to remain so.' Herschel expressed surprise that Dalton had been able to hit on his atomic theory without numberless experiments,[3] for to him the theory was 'the law of definite proportions, which is the same thing presented in a form divested of all hypothesis.' None the less he thought the theory the most important discovery since the laws of mechanics; but, like many of his contemporaries, he saw Dalton as the Kepler of chemistry. Dalton had discovered the simple laws according to which bodies combine; but he had erred in putting forward an hypothesis to explain these laws. What were required instead were mathematical relations, to be discovered by some Newton of chemistry, which would give the science a mathematical form.[4]

Chemists who were not satisfied with a science in which generalizations were painfully built up speculated less about atoms than about the status of the chemical elements. Davy's electrochemical researches were causing intense excitement just at the period when Dalton's atomic theory was published. Dalton could hardly have been called a glamorous or a dramatic figure; Davy was, and few would have disagreed with the reviewer in the *Philosophical Magazine* who called him 'the first chemist and philosopher of the age.'[5] Although Davy accepted definite proportions, and this made a considerable difference in his researches,[6] he rejected resolutely the atomic theory in the form in which Dalton put it forward. Exactly what Davy did believe about the structure of matter is worth investigating, because he had numerous successors, of whom Michael Faraday was the most distinguished.

In 1800, it seems fair to say, most chemists were corpuscularians, in the tradition of Newton and Boyle, although the rival atomism of Boscovich was by no means unknown.[7] Thus Davy wrote in his syllabus of lectures at the Royal Institution in 1802:

'The different bodies in nature are composed of particles or minute parts, individually imperceptible to the senses. When the particles are similar, the bodies they constitute are denominated simple, and when they are dissimilar, compound. The chemical phenomena result from the different arrangement of the particles of bodies; and the powers that produce these arrangements are repulsion, or the agency of heat, and attraction.'[8]

The simple bodies postulated by the corpuscularians might or might not have been the chemical elements, defined by Lavoisier as substances which resisted further chemical analysis. It was quite impossible to tell whether such bodies were made up of particles of only one kind or not. The answer that one gave would depend on the strength of one's belief in the simplicity of Nature. The same was true of the proposition that 'attraction' at the microscopic and macroscopic levels—'aggregation' and 'affinity,' and gravity—were all manifestations of one power.[9] Berthollet identified the attractive forces;[10] and so had Laplace,[11] though he realized that the atoms would have to be almost unimaginably small and dense to produce gravitational forces of the required magnitude. Laplace considered that the time for such generalizations had not yet come, because the laws of affinity were not yet known. In his view, affinity forces should be compared with the repulsive force of heat; he must have had in mind experiments on thermal decomposition. 'Some experiments already made with this view,' he concluded, 'afford us reason to hope that one day these laws will be perfectly known, and that then, by the application of analysis, the philosophy of terrestrial bodies may be brought to the same degree of perfection, which the discovery of universal gravitation has procured to astronomy.' Nobody could claim that this hope had been realized much before the last quarter of the nineteenth century.

In the last years of the eighteenth century, Guyton de Morveau also looked forward to a mathematical chemistry: 'the phenomena of combinations produced or destroyed are not the result of occult qualities, but of a rupture of equilibrium determined by forces which afford the hope of admeasurement by computation.'[12] And George Pearson, who translated the work of the French nomenclators, was also sanguine: 'that the same certainty as in mathematics may hereafter be attained in chemistry.'[13] Clearly Herschel had many predecessors who hoped chemistry would become mathematical.[14]

In this atmosphere, Dalton's theory was not generally treated as an *atomic* theory, but simply as laws of definite proportions. At first the theory did not arouse much attention at all;[15] and when it did the hypothetical part set many teeth on edge, and was often ignored as an eccentricity. Twenty years after the theory had been given to the world, Dalton was awarded a Royal Medal by the Royal Society, and it fell to Davy, as President, to make a speech[16] in which he said that the theory only became useful when its hypothetical parts had been removed.

It seems odd that Dalton, whose theory appears to have been derived from physical rather than chemical reasonings, should have aroused such opposition when he proposed an atomic theory to chemists who, for the most part, were corpuscularians already. For the position taken by Davy, that definite proportions were useful, while statements about atoms were both hypothetical and useless, was a very common one. Davy also thought that Dalton required the chemical elements to be the genuine elements of nature, the 'simple bodies' of the corpuscular philosophy, and not just substances that had so far not been analysed. The simplicity and grandeur of nature seemed compatible only with the unity of matter.

Some of Dalton's later writings illuminate the difference between his attitude and that of his opponents. Dalton had studied Newton, and copied out Query 31 from the *Opticks* in his notebook.[17] The example of Newton's work on gravity he produced 'to show that, however guarded we should be, not to let a theory or hypothesis, contradicted by experiment, mislead us; yet it is highly expedient to form some previous notion of the objects we are about, in order to direct us into some trains of enquiry.'[18] Hypotheses had an heuristic value, in Dalton's estimation, even if they had no wider usefulness; and it is interesting to see Newton introduced as an authority in favour of the hypothetico-deductive way of proceeding in science. Dalton went further than this in his claims for the atomic theory; in a letter to Berzelius he declared that without such a theory definite proportions would be 'mysterious.' He made the familiar comparison between chemistry and astronomy, but cast himself as Newton.[19] Definite proportions seemed to him 'like the *mystical ratios* of Kepler, which Newton so happily elucidated. The prosecution of the investigation can terminate, I conceive, in nothing but in the system which I adopt of particle applied to particle, as exhibited in my diagrams.' In his highly theoretical way, he wrote of Gay Lussac's investigations of gaseous combination that we should not 'be led to adopt these analyses till some reason can be discovered for them.'[20]

When Dalton published his theory, he received notable support at first from Wollaston's accurate researches on superacid and subacid salts. In this paper[21] of 1808, Wollaston appeared as strongly atomistic: 'all the facts that I had observed,' he wrote, 'are but particular instances of the more general observations of Mr Dalton, that in all cases the simple elements of bodies are disposed to unite atom to atom.' However, he was a more subtle and cautious thinker than Dalton, and he saw that a distinction should be made between the observed laws of combination and the models used in explanation. He tried to account for the ratios he found by the use of a model of spherical atoms;[22] and he wrote:

'I am further inclined to think, that when our views are sufficiently extended, to enable us to reason with precision concerning the proportions of elementary atoms, we shall find the arithmetical relation alone will not be sufficient to explain their mutual action, and that we shall be obliged to acquire a geometrical conception of their relative arrangement in all the three dimensions of solid extension.'

His meticulous approach would not allow him to confuse these speculations with solid experimental evidence; but in 1813 he published a paper[23] elaborating his atomic geometry. In the next year came a complete change, and we find him abandoning the attempt to achieve anything more than an arithmetical relationship. In the paper describing his slide-rule, or synoptic scale of chemical equivalents, he wrote:[24] 'When we estimate the relative weights of equivalents, Mr Dalton conceives that we are estimating the aggregate weights of a given number of atoms, and consequently the proportion which the ultimate single atoms bear to each other.' It appears that Wollaston could no longer agree, and Dalton's most powerful supporter relinquished his theory on the grounds that there are no means of telling which compounds are truly binary or ternary, so that there can never be any certainty of true atomic weights. Therefore equivalents must suffice.

Dalton had sought to escape from this difficulty by a number of simplicity axioms:[25] if only one compound between two elements was known, it must be assumed to be binary (of the form AB); if two were known, one must be binary and the other ternary (AB_2 or A_2B); and so on.[26] The axioms, whose arbitrary nature had been commented on adversely, notably by Bostock,[27] had led to the formula HO for water.

We should note that Wollaston's scepticism over atoms was confined to chemistry. For in chemistry the atomic theory appeared to postulate unnecessary entities whose weights were arbitrary and whose arrangements were inaccessible. Until the rise of structural organic chemistry, following Friedrich August Kekulé, Jacobus Henricus van't Hoff, Joseph Achille le Bel, and Johannes Wislicenus, hypotheses of atoms arranged in space were sterile, as Wollaston's earlier ideas had been. Later, Wollaston devised a physical experiment to establish that the earth's atmosphere was finite and therefore particulate.[28] If matter were a continuum, he supposed, then the earth's atmosphere would spread throughout space and all the heavenly bodies would have 'individual' unlimited atmospheres. Only if matter were of a limited divisibility would the earth's atmosphere have an upper limit. Astronomical observations showed that not all heavenly bodies had atmospheres, and this strongly suggested that the earth's atmosphere was finite and corpuscular. In fact this reasoning is erroneous because an infinite series can have a finite sum, and so the density of a continuous atmosphere could reach zero at a finite height. Wollaston was prepared to carry his argument forward into chemistry, for since the law of definite proportions had been found true for all kinds and phases of matter, 'we may without hesitation conclude that all those equivalent quantities, which we have learned to appreciate by proportionate numbers, *do really express the relative weights of elementary atoms, the ultimate objects of chemical research.'*[29] Many chemists felt unable to share Wollaston's confidence, perhaps because he had no proof that the particles or molecules of his argument were the Daltonian atoms.[30] After all, it was far safer, and equally useful, to stick to the synoptic scale of chemical equivalents!

Instead of the mathematical laws or purely formal theoretical entities that his contemporaries demanded, Dalton insisted on producing causal explanations and naïve models. The atomic theory in chemistry throughout the nineteenth century seems to have failed to appeal to those who wanted to make the subject mathematical. Wollaston's slide-rule for calculating equivalents, Benjamin Brodie's Calculus of Chemical Operations, and Ostwald's thermodynamic physical chemistry were all anti-atomic. These men would have agreed that: 'Theoretical physics became firmly established the day Newton rejected the scholastic precept of looking for causal explanations only, and realized instead that the chief, though not the sole, task of scientific theory is the discovery of the laws of phenomena.'[31] And surely they were right; Dalton could not explain any more than could his seventeenth-century corpuscularian predecessors, anything except definite proportions, and his theory simply pushed the explanation back one stage without adding anything to it. This is like the story that the earth was supported by an elephant, and the elephant by a tortoise; but one must not ask what held the tortoise up. In the latter part of the nineteenth century, the situation changed when the atomic theory, in the hands of Kekulé and his school, began to produce testable explanations and predictions of isomerism.

Dalton could hardly expect then to convince the more positivist of his critics, who found the theory cumbered with hypothesis where Dalton saw essential explanatory matter. Did he fare any better in his refutation of those like Davy who found the theory, in its acceptance of the elements as genuine 'simple bodies,' not hypothetical enough? Dalton never seems to have been able to make up his own mind on the question of whether his atomic theory was a theory of matter, that everything is made up of indestructible atoms of different kinds, or a theory only of 'chemical atoms.'

B

Davy certainly appears to have taken Dalton as intending the former meaning; but in 1810 Dalton had remarked:

> 'It has been imagined by some philosophers that all matter, however unlike, is probably the same thing; and that the great variety of its appearances arises from certain powers communicated to it, and from the variety of combinations and arrangements of which it is susceptible. From the notes I borrowed from Newton in the last lecture, this does not appear to have been his idea. Neither is it mine. I should apprehend there are a considerable number of what may be properly called *elementary* principles, which never can be metamorphosed, one into another, by any power we can control. We ought, however, to avail ourselves of every means to reduce the number of bodies or principles of this appearance as much as possible; and after all we may not know what elements are absolutely indecomposable, and what are refractory, because we do not apply the proper means for their reduction. We have already observed that all *atoms of the same kind*, whether simple or compound, must necessarily be conceived to be alike in shape, weight, and every other particular.'[32]

In this long quotation there are several important points. The first sentence is a summary of the views of Davy, at whom the passage is probably directed. But the disagreement with Davy is not as clear as it appears. For in the last sentence Dalton uses the term 'atom' with the adjectives 'simple' and 'compound.' A compound atom would be one of, say, carbon dioxide; this can be decomposed into its elements, certainly, but then it ceases to be carbon dioxide. The 'atom' of this substance is the smallest particle of it which is still carbon dioxide; what we call a 'molecule.' For Dalton here, 'atom' does not mean 'that which cannot be split,' but 'that which if split yields something qualitatively different.' One could still speak of atoms of nitrogen if, as many thought likely, this substance were shown to be a compound. The atomic theory, if this is what 'atom' means in it, is not a theory of matter at all; such 'chemical atoms,' mere units in chemical reactions, differ hardly at all from equivalents.

Dalton seems here to have surrendered in essence to his critics who used 'atom' and 'equivalent' interchangeably.

In the passage quoted Dalton differed from the majority of his predecessors in supposing that most of the elements were made up of simple atoms. It looks as though Dalton's conjecture was that these were not just chemical atoms, which resist analysis at present but might succumb to more formidable procedures, but genuine physical atoms. Dalton, like most of his contemporaries, wanted a simple world. As was written of electrical theories in 1813, 'the theoretical error of the present age may be that of attempting to simplify everything too far, and to refer numerous phenomena to one general law.'[33] It is therefore odd to find Dalton making his theory less palatable to his generation by admitting a considerable number of irreducibly different elementary bodies.

Dalton's theory as he proposed it had then a poor reception. And this reception was not unjustified, for Dalton's axioms were arbitrary, and his diagrams had little empirical foundation. By his rejection of Gay-Lussac's Law of Volumes he made further difficulties for his disciples. Wollaston and others rejected his views because atoms seemed unnecessary, and the correctness of their ideas is shown by the astonishing unfruitfulness of the specifically *atomic* theory until the 1860s.

In the generation that followed Dalton, Davy and Wollaston, chemists took various lines. A few, like Faraday, rejected corpuscular atoms on the evidence of new experimental phenomena; or, like Prout and Dumas, rejected simple atomism for a molecular theory of matter on the grounds of the interpretation of the chemical laws of combination; or, like William Whewell, rejected atoms because 'chemical research has not afforded, nor can afford, any satisfactory evidence whatever'[34] for such hypothetical entities. The positivists were joined by physicists, whose atomic theories postulated few different kinds of atom.

Only a minority, such as Charles Daubeny, the Professor of Chemistry at Oxford, gave general support to the atomic theory, although even he was tempted by Prout's molecular speculations into a position not unlike that of Dumas.[35] The atomic theory, he wrote, 'affords a key which exactly corresponds to a very complicated series of effects; and hence, though it wants that complete evidence that would be afforded, if we could know the existence of the cause, yet it may claim at least our assent, until another be proposed more adequate to account for the phenomena.'[36]

The majority of chemists, while using the term 'atom,' refused to commit themselves to the real existence of such bodies, and since this attenuated form of atomism seems to have been adopted in most of the textbooks written in the half-century or so after Dalton's publication, we shall call it the 'textbook tradition.' Thus William Thomas Brande wrote that 'the atomic doctrine or theory of definite proportionals has been much blended with hypothetical views, but it will be most satisfactorily and usefully considered as an independent collection of facts.'[37] More interesting was the attack on this school made by the Irish chemist Michael Donovan in 1832. He argued that the atomic theory and the law of equivalents involved the same assumptions, and therefore were equally hypothetical.

'It has been supposed by some that the doctrine of determinate proportions is a mere expression of the facts, and essentially different from the atomic hypothesis. . . . It appears to me, that there is as much hypothesis in one doctrine as in the other. We say that an indivisible atom of hydrogen 1 combines with an indivisible atom of oxygen 8. . . . Here there are three gratuitous assumptions: first that the combining quantities are atoms; secondly that they are indivisible; and thirdly that the bodies combine atoms to atom. But in the doctrine which professes to embody facts, we can detect the same three assumptions, tacitly involved.'[38]

No one else, at this period, seems to have taken this view.

In the mid-century, the unity of matter school was much encouraged by the work of the spectroscopists who had recently begun to investigate the spectra of the heavenly bodies. This work followed the suggestion[39] that the dark lines in the solar and stellar spectra must be due to the presence of bodies in the atmosphere of the sun and stars that would give bright lines at the same frequencies in their arc spectra. In 1864, the chemist William Allen Miller[40] and the astronomer William Huggins[41] published papers[42] on the spectra of planets, fixed stars, and later, nebulae. In a nebula the most exciting observation was made; a bright nitrogen line was visible, while other lines of this element, which should have been equally obvious, could not be found. Huggins asked whether this one line indicated a form of matter (which he named 'nebulium') more elementary than nitrogen.[43] In 1873, Norman Lockyer suggested that the high temperatures of the stars and nebulae might cause the earthly 'elements' to dissociate into simpler substances and thereby give rise to complex spectra.[44] These spectroscopists had then come to a position like that of Davy—perhaps because both he and they were handling new analytical techniques— and their view slowly became accepted among other workers in the field.

In their attitude towards atomism the chemists of the 1860s had therefore various traditions on which to draw. Many clung to a moderately positivist position, holding that the atomic theory was useful though perhaps not true. Of those who opposed the theory, an important group inherited the idea that Nature, being harmonious and simple, would not have required numerous different species of matter from which to construct the world. In a sense, they were vindicated by the development of atomic physics at the end of the century. Sir Benjamin Collins Brodie, who set off the discussions on atomism that came to a head in 1869, in his 'Calculus of Chemical Operations' and his *Ideal Chemistry*, was in this tradition, and in that which held that chemistry must become mathematical; he was also strongly positivist in outlook. His papers should therefore have pleased those who opposed atomism on any of these three grounds.

BRODIE'S IDEAL CHEMISTRY

Brodie began as a believer in atoms, and indeed in a paper[45] of 1850, he discussed the chemical elements and concluded that 'under certain conditions, there exists a chemical difference between the particles of which they consist.' This difference was a kind of polarization; and that the elements formed particle to particle links might be, he thought, evidence of their complex structure. The paper represents an attempt to reconcile an electrical theory of valency with the chemical theory which demanded that *like* atoms adhered to one another. However, by the 1860s Brodie had become an opponent of the atomists, and become a dangerous adversary when he proposed a new set of symbols for chemistry which took into account the laws of chemical combination without lending themselves, as Wollaston's equivalents had, to an atomic interpretation.

In 1866, after public encouragement from Odling,[46] Brodie published in the *Philosophical Transactions* the first part of his 'Calculus of Chemical Operations'[47] in which he declared that Dalton's atomic theory no longer explained the facts of chemistry, and that in his Calculus such hypothetical entities as atoms would not appear. The clearest exposition of Brodie's Ideal Chemistry was given by its author before the Chemical Society in 1867.[48] He then stated that he believed theory to be essential to the existence of chemistry, for the science had only begun with the phlogiston theory; but he noted that Davy had made his great discoveries without a theory, and instead 'rested content with the facts of numerical analysis and the laws of combination deduced from them.'[49] Dalton's theory was in fact more audacious than the phlogiston theory because it postulated that the observed continuity of matter was an illusion. In the sixty years since the theory came out, chemistry had seen plenty of change, but no progress. Brodie had recently seen advertised a set of balls and wires for building up models of molecules, and this seemed to him the last straw. That the atomic theory should have resulted in such a 'thoroughly materialistic bit of joiner's work' proved that chemistry had gone off the rails of philosophy, for such a bathos could only have come from a whole series of errors and misconceptions.[50] In place of this then, Brodie proposed his Calculus, whose object was 'to discover what is the nature and the number of operations by which chemical substances are made or constructed,' and to bring chemists under rules in which their symbols, unlike the existing ones, would have agreed and distinct meanings, and be combined under definite laws.[51]

Brodie noted that according to his system, there were three distinct categories of elements. First were those like hydrogen, a, produced in *one* operation. Next came those made in two or more *similar* operations, like oxygen, ξ^2. The third and largest class was made in two or more *different* operations; an example was chlorine, whose symbol was $a\chi^2$. This last class was rather exciting, for the symbol of chlorine was very similar to that of the compound, hydrogen peroxide, $a\xi^2$. Did it mean that elements like the halogens, nitrogen and phosphorus were *compounds* of unknown elements with hydrogen? Did the substances symbolized by χ^2 or by χ really exist? Although the symbols were not necessarily of real physical things, they were not unreal either, for they had not just come out of Brodie's head. So he called them 'ideal,' like geometrical entities, and his system became 'Ideal Chemistry.' There was no need to speculate on the reality of the subelementary units. But, abandoning his positivism, Brodie did so; and by shifting his ground in this way, and allowing the Calculus to have a predictive value, he unconsciously laid himself open to the charge which he had levelled at the atomists; namely that χ, ξ, θ, etc., were postulates for which there was at present no evidence, and were strikingly similar to atoms.[52]

In the process, Brodie foreshadowed Crookes's theory of the evolution of the chemical elements.[53] He was probably influenced here by the American mineralogist and anti-atomist, Thomas Sterry Hunt, who stayed with him at Oxford in May 1867 after a visit to Paris where he had witnessed and discussed Henri Sainte-Claire Deville's experiments on dissociation.[54] At the end of May, Hunt lectured at the Royal Institution on 'The Chemistry of the Primeval Earth' in which he made the sensational suggestion that the decomposition or dissociation of compounds under intense heat was of general application, so that in stellar and nebulous masses, dissociation of the elements into a more elemental matter took place.[55] One week later, Brodie gave his Ideal Chemistry lecture to the Chemical Society and reversed Hunt's suggestions into a theory of association, or genesis. When the earth was being formed, Brodie suggested, substances like χ might have existed in the form of perfect gases. As the temperature fell these would have combined, and some forms of matter might have become stable to the exclusion of others; some indeed *so* stable that their decomposition could not again occur. But we might hope to find such bodies as χ in the stars and nebulae. Brodie noted Miller and Huggins's speculations and, more encouragingly, that few of the elements detected in the sun were of the third type; perhaps the sun was too hot for them to be formed.

As an alternative to atomism Brodie's Calculus was a failure, but it did much to encourage discussion about the status of hypothetical entities in an experimental science like chemistry; and it aroused a tremendous interest in the nature of the chemical elements and, among those who subscribed to the atomic-molecular theory, in the nature of the atom itself. When Brodie's lecture was republished in 1880, Henry Armstrong, in a review in *Nature*,[56] singled out for praise the anticipation of Lockyer's 'working hypothesis.' By then, for many years, Lockyer had been attempting to observe a dissociation of the elements in his laboratory. Although his conclusions were original, he could not have failed to have learned of Brodie's speculations since the two of them collaborated in 1874 on experiments which involved the dissociation of ozone and, perhaps, other elements.[57] Unfortunately, no details of these experiments were recorded. In view of the persistence of the idea of the complexity of the elements among chemists in the nineteenth century, it is surprising that Lockyer's dissociation hypothesis, and his identification of helium, should have met with so much opposition from chemists and physicists.[58] When Lockyer claimed to the Royal Society at the end of 1878 that he had successfully induced dissociation of the elements in the laboratory, there was a furious discussion of the implication that the atom had structure.[59] Clearly, by then, chemists had become less sceptical of atoms.

Crookes's headline over his report of Brodie's lecture in *Chemical News*[60] was 'The Chemistry of the Future,' with no question mark. Even outside chemistry, Brodie's notion of the atomic theory as an inefficient kind of abacus was bound to arouse attention, and in 1868 an anonymous article on 'The Atomic Theory of Lucretius' appeared in the *North British Review*.[61] The author, Fleeming Jenkin, claimed that the question of atoms was now as open as ever. Speculation on the issue was sometimes treated as impious, but the wave theory of light had led to new discoveries, and so might an atomic theory. In William Thomson's vortex theory the continuous fluid school of physicists had, rather oddly, arrived at atomism of a kind;[62] but in chemistry the support given to the theory by Dalton, who had made it 'heretical' to doubt atoms, had been undermined by Brodie's ideas which 'seem independent if not subversive to the simple atomic faith.'

THE CHEMICAL SOCIETY PRESIDENTIAL LECTURE OF 1869

Among English scientists Auguste Comte's only disciple was the defender of atoms, Alexander Williamson,[63] who believed that atomism was a verifiable hypothesis, not a logical artifice, because empirical support and reasoning could be marshalled for it. But what kind of support? After all, the atom was too minute to *see*. And yet seeing the atom was for some extreme positivists the only possible verification of the atomic theory.[64] It was certainly not this kind of verification that Williamson had in mind, but rather (to use an expression of Whewell's) that he could marshal a solid consilience of inductions for it.

Williamson's belief in the atomic theory was expressed very forcibly in his famous Presidential Address that was delivered to the London Chemical Society on 3 June 1869. The title of the lecture was 'On the Atomic Theory,' and in its day, it was 'generally regarded as the best exposition and defence of the doctrine yet made, and which may be consulted with profit by those desiring to obtain a clear statement of the principal research adduced for its confirmation.'[65] But when it is read today, its loose organization makes it rather dull reading unless something is known of the tide of scepticism it was designed to abate, and of the extraordinary discussion to which it gave rise in the autumn.

Williamson's contention was that it was time to accept the atomic theory unreservedly: atoms existed, the atomic theory gave a clear and consistent explanation of the facts, and it had valuable predictive powers.[66] Reading from a handful of unarranged notes,[67] Williamson professed himself shocked by the scepticism of his fellow chemists as disclosed by their textbook statements. After ineffectively quoting from several (without mentioning author or title[68]), he declared:

'It certainly does seem strange that men accustomed to consult nature by experiment so constantly as chemists do, should make use of a system of ideas of which such things can be said. I think I am not overstating the fact, when I say that, on the one hand, all chemists use the atomic theory, and that on the other hand, a considerable number of them view it with mistrust, some with positive dislike.'[69]

This was a poor state of affairs thought Williamson; a theory utilized, but privately discredited, or treated with reservations. If the atomic theory was so bad, then it was time it was replaced by something better. If not, then it deserved praise as 'among the best and most precious trophies which the human mind has earned.'[70] For such reasons, Williamson felt that the case in favour of the atomic theory should now be put.[71]

His long review of the evidence for the atomic-molecular theory, which was by no means so cogently and brilliantly argued as Brodie's lecture two years before, was made from three main standpoints: the doctrines of equivalent weights, of molecules, and of valency.[72] From each level, he was able to find support for atomism and hence claim an over-all strong case for the atomic theory. As an example of Williamson's brief, we shall consider his discussion of equivalent weights.[73]

After reminding his audience how equivalent weights are defined relative to the unit weight of hydrogen, and how the same element could have more than one equivalent, Williamson turned to the law of multiple proportions, which Dalton had explained with atoms. What was the evidence for this law? And with what proof, if any, did the law provide the atomic theory? Like Donovan nearly forty years previously, Williamson pointed out that there were involved in the very foundation of the law, hypothetical assumptions only justified by the law's agreement with a great number of experiments.[74] The law seemed to be a valid generalization for simple inorganic substances, but did that justify its application to some of the complex substances of organic chemistry? Williamson believed it did, but he wanted to point out the assumption involved. For organic substances the proportional numbers were often quite high, so that a single quantitative analysis by itself could not decide the chemist in favour of one empirical formula rather than another.[75] From single experiments the only conclusions would have been that *some* elements in simple compounds were capable of uniting with one another in simple multiples of *certain* weights. But Williamson knew of no chemist who limited the law of multiple proportions in that way (*i.e.*, to equivalents).

'It is applied to all elements and to all compounds of them, in spite of the fact that the usual results of observation require *straining* to agree with any multiple formula, and the common majority of substances have not yet been reduced by the process to any definite formula whatsoever.'[76]

Therefore, Williamson strongly criticized those chemists who, following tradition, claimed that the law of multiple proportions was a direct representation of experimental facts, whereas the atomic theory was a hypothesis independent of the law. He was able to carry Donovan's point over into the contemporary practice of the organic chemist.

'The actual process by which we establish the composition of such complex bodies is by *assuming* that the composition of each of them must correspond to entire multiples of the atomic weights of their elements, and by treating as errors of observation any divergence between the proportions discovered by analysis and such atomic proportions.'[77]

These presuppositions unveiled, with what evidence did the law of multiple proportions provide the atomic theory? Atomism, he thought, gave a consistent and satisfactory explanation of variable equivalents, but the law certainly did not necessarily imply the atomic theory. It would have been possible, and logically consistent, to express say carbon monoxide and dioxide by the formulae CO and $C_{\frac{1}{2}}O$ instead of CO and CO_2. This would allow the present carbon 'atom' to be divisible, and

'as far as the proportion of the elements is concerned, we have no better right to suppose the carbon is indivisible, and that the acid contains twice as much oxygen as the oxide, than we have to suppose that the carbon is divisible, and that half of the carbon is taken out of the carbonic oxide in forming carbonic acid.'[78]

Of course, this was saying no more than that the elements possessed more than one equivalent whose values were obtained by dividing the atomic weights by the valency; *e.g.*, C, C/2, Fe/2, Fe/3. However, it did enable Williamson again to press the point that whenever the law of multiple proportions was mentioned, chemists did not refer to fractional expressions like Fe/2, C/4, Cu/2, etc., but to the normal atomic symbols.

> 'They describe in fact *atoms* as occurring thus combined with one another in the proportions of entire multiples of their weights; in fact the so-called law of multiple proportions has no existence apart from the atomic theory; those who adopt it seem not to be aware that they are using the notion of atoms, or else they are shy of mentioning it.'[79]

Nevertheless, Williamson was prepared to admit that the fact of varying equivalents *by itself* was as much evidence against the atomic theory as for it. Yet, he claimed, no chemist had ever used such variations in this way. Instead, when one of these sceptics

> 'has ascertained by analysis the percentage composition of a compound, and wants to find its formula, he divides the percentage weight of each element by its *atomic weight*. He seeks for the smallest integral numbers which represent the proportion of atoms, and he attributes to impurity of his sample or to errors of analysis any deviation from the atomic formula thus obtained. He looks to the reaction of the body for aid in constructing his atomic formula and controls his analyses by considerations derived from well established reactions, but whenever he is led by any of these considerations to a formula which contains a fraction of any atomic weight, he takes a multiple of the formula sufficiently high to be entirely free from such fractions. In no case does he reason on a basis independent of the atomic theory.'[80]

Having pointed out the hypothetical assumptions involved in the 'factual' law of multiple proportions, and having admitted that it by no means proved atomism, Williamson reminded his audience that a system should not be judged solely on the evidence of *one* of its parts.[81] This led him on to discuss at length additional support for atomism from the doctrines of molecules and valency.

Williamson considered his case proved and the opponent's case a mere negation and therefore valueless. Surely here was a golden opportunity to have tackled the challenge laid down by Brodie in the 'Chemical Calculus'? But mysteriously, despite the evidence that his lecture was originally designed as a reply to Brodie,[82] Williamson ignored it.

What was the atom? How should it be visualized? Did it have structure? In answer to such obvious questions, Williamson took the pragmatic line of Lavoisier and Kekulé. The chemical atom, like the element for Lavoisier, was no absolute term.

'In using the atomic language and atomic ideas, it seems to me of great importance that *we should limit our words as much as possible to statements of facts*, and put aside into the realm of imagination all that is not in evidence. Thus the question whether our elementary atoms are in their nature indivisible, or whether they are built up of smaller particles, is one upon which I, as a chemist, have no hold whatever, and *I may say that in chemistry the question is not raised by any evidence whatsoever.*'[83]

Quite clearly the word *atom*, when it was applied to the elements, simply denoted the *fact* that they had not been decomposed under any known conditions.[84] Whether the atom was divisible, possessed structure or not, was not for the time being a chemical question, but a metaphysical one. All Williamson claimed was that there did exist least particles of a chemical nature which combined together to produce the chemical phenomena that he had so carefully reviewed. Chemistry demanded a corpuscular language of interpretation, and atomism was the most consistent explanation of the facts. But whether the atom was a solid ball, or an etherial vortex, Williamson 'knew nothing about it.'[85]

THE AUTUMN DEBATE OF 1869

The Presidential lecture had been planned to abate the tide of atomic scepticism, so Williamson must have been surprised when he found the opposition unconverted. There was no time for any discussion after his long lecture,[86] or at the next meeting of the Chemical Society when Dumas delivered the inaugural Faraday lecture. But at the final meeting that summer, an organic chemist, Edmund J. Mills, presented some criticisms of Williamson's address.[87] 'No discussion followed [Mills's paper] but the President [Williamson] said he should feel honoured if, after seeing in print what he himself had put together on the subject, they thought it worth while to go into the question some evening.'[88] This suggestion was acted upon at the earliest opportunity, namely at the first meeting of the Society after the summer vacation, on 4 November, when a 'Discussion of Dr Williamson's Lecture on the Atomic Theory' was held.[89] Oddly, it does not seem that this meeting attracted anything like the same attention as Brodie's earlier lecture. The *Chemical News* did not publicize the meeting, ran no editorials, and only published an abstract of the discussion instead of the previous 'veritable *tour de force* of the shorthand writer.'[90] Nevertheless, the discussion, in which the participants included Williamson, Brodie, Edward Frankland,[91] William Odling,[92] Miller, John Tyndall,[93] George Carey Foster,[94] and Edmund Mills,[95] was afterwards described, like Brodie's lecture, as 'a memorable and interesting evening in the life of the Chemical Society.'[96]

The occasion must have had an aura of theatre about it, for with dramatic irony, the roles of Brodie and Williamson in 1867 were reversed with Brodie in the Chair. The biased Chairman immediately re-established his own dislike of the atomic theory; and like a good disciple of Gerhardt and positivism, he urged that chemistry would be well rid of structural conceits since these deluded 'chemists into the belief that they understood things about which they knew nothing.'[97] The abstract of Brodie's remarks suggests that he only hinted at his Calculus by arguing that chemistry could only be based upon such experimental phenomena as the laws of gaseous combination, or atomic heats. Hypotheses about the physical divisibility of matter had to be separated from such facts, and the separation of *facts* from *fiction* was something that Williamson had failed to do.

Williamson naturally claimed that he had never confused the two. Brodie and he were not talking the same language, for their presuppositions were poles apart: a positivist versus a pragmatist. Once more Williamson stated that his sole aim had been to give the *chemical* evidence for atoms and molecules. A variety of independent chemical observations corroborated the theory which formed a 'perfectly homogeneous whole.' Beyond the chemical evidence he was content to be as pragmatic as Lavoisier and Kekulé, for 'whether the particles of matter have a spherical form or not, whether they are in their nature indivisible, whether they are in reality the ultimate atoms of matter . . . he knew not, nor did such questions exist for him as a chemist.'[98]

However, this pragmatic defence was insufficient for some of Williamson's colleagues assembled at Burlington House. Frankland, still a sceptic, opposed any realist approach. Unlike Williamson, he taunted, he was 'no blind believer in atoms.' Yet, since there did not seem to be, for the moment, any better explanation of chemical phenomena, it was right to use it as a 'kind of ladder to assist the chemist.'[99] We saw that this conventionalism had been attacked by Williamson in his lecture, and it now rather surprisingly called down the wrath of Brodie. It was nonsense to employ a theory in which you did not believe, or were willing to deny while exploiting its successes to the full. Brodie could agree with Williamson here. It was all or nothing: either one accepted atomism because one believed atoms existed, or one rejected atoms completely. There was no room for utilitarian compromise or for the Comtean claim that the atomic hypothesis was a useful logical artifice. Here, Frankland and Brodie illustrate two antagonistic aspects of the positivist's attitude towards theoretical entities: the extreme phenomenalists[100] who only deal with observables, and the moderate conventionalists[101] who are prepared to employ them as useful fictions.

Odling, who represents our 'textbook tradition,' also continued to be sceptical of atoms.[102] He agreed with Frankland that the continuity or discontinuity of matter was a metaphysical question, but he did not think Williamson's lecture had shown that at all. Odling implied that Williamson claimed that chemical facts pointed to *the* discontinuity of matter, whereas of course, what Williamson had said, or meant to say, was that *a* discontinuity was shown. Odling could not agree that all chemists' actions were coloured by the atomic theory, and he sought support from Davy's Dalton address of 1826. The laws of combination, he said quoting Davy, were like Kepler's laws of planetary motion, simply generalizations from observation; the atomic theory was superinduced upon them. Tyndall neatly turned the tables on Odling by pointing out that Newton had 'superinduced' the acceptable gravitational theory upon Kepler's laws.[103] Many years later Odling became a convinced atomist. At a banquet held by the Chemical Society in 1898, he publicly admitted that he had been mistaken to question Williamson's stand in 1869. Modestly, he said that he had always been content to follow in Williamson's footsteps, but that unfortunately he had more than once lagged some way behind.[104]

It was now the turn of those who, for one reason or another, tended to side with Williamson in the controversy. Ironically, this support came chiefly from the physicists, although in his lecture Williamson had paid scant attention to their arguments for atomism from kinetic theory.[105] Miller, the spectroscopist, argued the useful fiction case from the atomist's side. The human mind demanded that we *explain* any extensive series of phenomena. If we did not have the atomic theory then the laws of chemical combination would have to be explained some other way, and so far, as Williamson had said, no one had devised any alternative.[106] Those who criticized had a duty to try and devise something equally good. Miller then repeated the parallel drawn by Jenkin in the *North British Review*; the wave theory of light was quite generally accepted by physicists, yet it was in a similar position in physics to the atomic theory in chemistry. However, the physicists did not create a fuss about it!

The physicist John Tyndall thought Miller's wave theory analogy extremely apt. It would be easy for an Odling-type physicist to say that the wave theory had been superimposed upon the simple phenomena of light, and hence that it was a mere fiction. But physicists were evidently better behaved than chemists, and the wave theory would stand so long as it explained all the facts. Tyndall returned to elaborate this point at the British Association the following year.

'Many chemists of the present day refuse to speak of atoms and molecules as real things. Their caution leads them to stop short of the clear, sharp, mechanically intelligible atomic theory . . . and to make the doctrine of multiple proportions their intellectual bourne. I respect their caution, though I thing it here misplaced. The chemists who recoil from these notions of atoms and molecules accept without hesitation, the Undulatory Theory of Light. Like you and me they one and all believe in an ether and its light producing waves.'[107]

Perhaps the most interesting contribution came from George Carey Foster, a chemistry pupil of Williamson's who had turned physicist and become Professor of Physics at University College, London. No one present, he thought, wanted to deny that the atomic theory was useful; what they had to argue was whether the theory was true, and whether Williamson had proved this. The utilitarianism of Miller was all very well, but rather beside the point since one had only to look at the history of science to notice repeatedly erroneous theories which had been most useful in their day, e.g., the phlogiston theory of combustion, and (added Tyndall) the corpuscular theory of light. Foster then momentarily placed the whole discussion on a higher plane by pointing out that preconceptions concerning chemical composition forced the chemist to explain chemical phenomena corpuscularly. We think of a 'compound' as composed of its elements. Consider mercuric sulphide: automatically we presuppose that the mercury and sulphur occupy separate portions of space—that there is no interpenetration of these elements. Hence by mental division, we can separate mercury and sulphur from out of the smallest conceivable portion of cinnabar. However, if we could remove such corpuscular preconceptions, the process of chemical change that occurred when mercury 'combined' with sulphur might very well be conceived in some other manner.[108]

'We know that between the bodies which disappear and the body which appears, there are certain relations, not only qualitative but quantitative, the total mass of the disappearing substance being equal to that of the appearing substances; but we may perhaps return, sometimes, at any rate, with great benefit, to the notion that one portion of matter is actually transmuted into another; that it ceases to exist as such, but something else comes in place of it. From such ideas the existence of atoms would not follow of necessity, *but with our present mode of stating and reasoning about chemical changes, an atomic hypothesis or basis appears to be inevitable.*'[109]

Possibly Foster had in mind Brodie's recent efforts, or even the older explanations of chemical change attempted by Aristotle and the alchemists, and evident in Naturphilosophie.[110]

Such a system of chemical Naturphilosophie had been already developed by Brodie's friend Sterry Hunt, who rejected 'all hypotheses regarding the constitution of matter, as irrelevant to the study of chemistry.'[111] Following Kant, Hegel and Oken, Hunt believed that chemical combination was not a preformation but an epigenesis, 'not a putting together of molecules, but an interpenetration of masses.'[112] The model and basis for all chemical union was *solution*. One particular feature of past chemical processes had been Stoichiogeny, or the production of chemical elements from 'a primal undifferentiated matter.'[113] The first steps in this field of research had been taken by Dumas,[114] thought Hunt, and closely followed by the simultaneous suggestions of Brodie and himself in 1867; long before the much publicized conceptions of genesis which had been recently evoked by Mills and Crookes. Like his mentor, J. B. Stallo, Hunt deplored the transference of the kinetic theory into chemistry, and at the Priestley celebrations in Pennsylvania in 1874, he declared:

'Are we not going beyond the limits of a sound philosophy when we endeavor by hypotheses of hard particles with void spaces, of atoms and molecules with bonds and links, to explain chemical affinities; and when we give a concrete form to our mechanical conception of the great laws of definite and multiple proportions to which the chemical process is subordinated? Let us not confound the image with the thing itself, until, in the language of Brodie, in the discussion of this very question, "we mistake the suggestions of fancy for the reality of nature, and cease to distinguish between conjecture and fact." '[115]

Although Hunt's unconventional analysis of chemical change as 'the actual mutability of matter'[116] provoked little discussion in either America or Europe,[117] it should not be thought that these ideas were merely eccentric. For as a mineralogical chemist, Hunt's primary interests were complex substances like the molybdates and silicates whose stoichiometric rationalization sorely tried many a chemist's faith in atomism before the advent of X-ray analysis.

The final reported speech at the 1869 debate by Edmund Mills was also of a philosophical nature, but the abstractor has so compressed his speech as to make it incomprehensible unless reference is made to the series of erudite papers which he published beginning in 1867.[118] All the sciences, he claimed, converged to a common limit, or 'a most general idea.' He longed for the law from which *all* phenomena might be deduced; but the most general idea against which all scientific ideas should be measured was, at the present time, *motion*. He tried to illustrate this by a discussion of acidity and alkalinity. Davy was applauded because, having first considered hydrogen as the acidifying principle, he afterwards held 'that the acidity of a substance is a kind of resultant whose direction is hydrogen.' Despite this imaginative gloss on Davy, Mills had to deplore that no satisfactory dynamical notion of an acid was yet available, and be content to remark that acidity and alkalinity were relative terms.

In his application of his 'universal criterion' to atomism, Mills had an approach that was far from empirical. He referred to Davy, Wollaston and Faraday as those whose arguments against atomism had never been answered, and he repeated Davy's empirical arguments for the complexity of the chemical elements.[119] Isomerism was not explained by atomists, for space and position could only be relative, and to talk of position in empty space was to talk nonsense. Assertions about indivisibles, which had neither observation nor analogy to support them, could give no explanation, and neither could inadequately defined phrases. Instead the chemist had to show any phenomenon to be an instance of known and general phenomena. The law of definite proportions was tinged with an element of continuity; there were mechanical mixtures, definite compounds, and indefinite compounds like albumen. The law did not necessitate atoms, for definite ratios between curves going off to infinity were perfectly possible, and continuous substances could similarly have definite combining ratios. 'Surrounded on all sides with continuity, motion, and change,' he wrote, 'our most popular ideas relate to limits, repose, and stability.' The atomic theory was one of these. The atomic and phlogiston theories might aptly be compared (as Brodie had done); atoms were invisible, so had been phlogiston; and atomic weights had changed with no less facility than the properties of phlogiston. Mills concluded that 'the atomic theory has no experimental basis, is untrue to nature generally, and consists in the main of a materialistic fallacy, derived from appetite more than from judgment.'[120]

Such arguments, like those of Sterry Hunt, may make interesting reading, but we cannot imagine that they had much effect on the working organic chemists who had happily applied the ideas of valency and molecular structure to their otherwise intractable subject. In fact, we have it on record that Mills, although a competent and sometimes brilliant practical chemist, was dismissed as a metaphysician when it came to theory.[121]

THE AFTERMATH

There was one spokesman who was present at the 1869 meeting but was not reported. This was the organic chemist Colin Alder Wright, a pupil of Henry Roscoe and Carl Schorlemmer, and a pioneer of alkaloid chemistry.[122] As it turned out, Wright brought the controversy over the atomic theory before the Chemical Society for a third time in a protracted dispute with Williamson's assistant, Robert William Atkinson. Wright held to extreme views in the textbook tradition over what was fact and hypothesis in chemistry. How this applied to the new structural chemistry he made the subject of a long paper read to the Chemical Society in February 1872.[123] Like Brodie, he believed that the atomic theory had only been

'a mechanical conception suited, doubtlessly, to an age when an accurate knowledge of facts was only beginning to exist, these facts being of a nature difficult to grasp without some *material* aid, but not possessed of such advantages when the knowledge of these facts and their correlations becomes somewhat more extended; that it is unnecessary to express any facts, and incompetent (without *much* patching and botching) to explain many generalizations, where the measurement of force of some kind is a necessary datum; hence the conclusion is drawn that it is undesirable that the ideas and language of this hypothesis should occupy the prominent and fundamental part in chemical philosophy now attributed to them.'[124]

Wright aimed to show two things. First, that the main facts and generalizations upon which chemistry was founded could be expressed in words, or represented by symbols, without in any way involving the use of an hypothesis of material atoms; and second, that although the atomic hypothesis supplied a clear *raison d'être* of such facts and generalizations, it did not account for all of them. Thus like Brodie, Wright claimed that atomism was both unnecessary and insufficient; but unlike Brodie, he believed that 'the *ordinary* symbols do not necessarily involve the atomic hypothesis at all—that, by suitably choosing definitions, the symbol may be employed and yet the mind of the chemist be free from the atomic doctrine.'[125]

The *Chemical News* was able to report, for the third time, that 'a long and very interesting discussion ensued.'[126] Frankland and Mills were present among others, but only Heinrich Debus appears to have tried to defend atomism. Wright concluded in the manner of Brodie that the proper use of atomism was as 'an algebraic expression of facts rather than as an hypothesis, and although he could not go so far as Dr Mills in considering it a chemical evil, he had no doubt that a textbook could be written without the employment of the atomic theory.'[127]

Wright was not left unchallenged by the Williamson set; Atkinson dissected Wright's arguments before the Chemical Society in May,[128] and claimed that Wright had used the atomic theory, or at least been unconsciously guided by it, even though he asserted that it was unnecessary. As for its insufficiency, the answer was that the theory had still to be developed, and its past successes promised well for its future power. Wright was able to make a spontaneous reply, but left the elaborations for an extremely skilful written answer.[129]

However, the details of this later controversy need not detain us, for, not surprisingly, these polemics made no startling conversions of either party. Williamson's own impression was evidently that no one had found any fallacy in the evidence which he had presented for atomism. In his Presidential Address to the British Association at Bradford in 1873 he still continued to level the same three objections against the anti-atomists that he had used in 1869.

> '1. That these objectors have not shown us any inconsistency in the atomic theory, nor in the conclusions to which it leads.
> 2. That neither these nor any other philosophers have been able to explain the facts of chemistry on the assumption that there are no atoms, but that matter is infinitely divisible.
> 3. That when they interpret their analyses, these chemists allow themselves neither more nor less latitude than the Atomic Theory allows; in fact they are unconsciously guided by it.'[130]

Concerning this, a reviewer in the *Athenaeum* wrote:

> 'What he [Williamson] has to say about atoms he brings to conclusion by defending the Atomic Theory against the attacks of certain modern chemists. Poor Dr Wright! We fear that he may yet be smarting under some of the President's incisive remarks.'[131]

This reference to Wright, which perhaps indicates that Brodie's work had been forgotten already, drew forth a dignified reply from him, together with a counterattack upon Williamson's Bradford speech.

> 'Speaking for myself, I fail to see the cogency of the reasons which lead a great number of modern chemists to the impression that matter can only be viewed as being made up of "atoms" of some sixty-five essentially different kinds; these atoms, when connected together in certain ill-defined ways, constituting the "molecules" of which the innumerable compounds now known are conceived as being made up.'[132]

The positivist textbook tradition remained his deepest conviction.

'In teaching the science of chemistry it is preferable, first, to enumerate the *facts* in language independent of any hypothesis, and then to enunciate the various hypotheses that have been and are held, showing how far each is in accordance or contradiction with the observed facts; rather than to mix up from the outset one particular hypothesis with the facts, so as finally to impress on the mind the manifestly erroneous conclusion that the facts have no evidence apart from the hypothesis that more or less clearly explains them.'[133]

Wright's old antagonist, Atkinson, replied among other points that 'it is not just to assert that the atomic theory is incapable of explaining certain chemical phenomena if no data are at hand by which the necessary connexion between them can be established. It will be time enough to reject the theory when it has been proved that it ought to explain such phenomena and fails to do so.'[134] At this point the *Athenaeum*'s editor wisely closed the issue, but Crookes continued to fan the flames in his weekly *Chemical News*.[135]

One thing that these long discussions between 1866 and 1874 had accomplished was to bring out sharply, for all to see, the undercurrent of atomic scepticism which had beset chemistry since the beginning of the century. In an editorial, the new weekly scientific journal *Nature* remarked of the 1869 debate:

'The general theoretical tone of the discussion last Thursday must have surprised most who were present. Our own position is necessarily an impartial one; but it will probably be agreed that between the parties there is a gulf, deeper and wider than at first appears, and perhaps unprovided with a bridge.'[136]

Nature was unduly pessimistic, even though the gulf did widen for a time, especially among physical chemists who attempted to explain chemical phenomena in terms of thermodynamics instead of atoms;[137] for a bridge was ultimately found in the early years of the present century, but only at the expense of giving structure to the atom through the efforts of the unity of matter school.[138]

However, it is certainly true that until the work of the organic structural and synthetic chemists, and the stereochemists of the 1870s and 1880s, an adequate and consistent *nonatomic* chemistry was a distinct possibility. Although the tetrahedral carbon atom was proposed by van't Hoff and le Bel before Part II of Brodie's Calculus was published in 1877, it was virtually ignored until Wislicenus demonstrated its power in 1888.[139] Before this chemists had only recognized the problem of structural isomerism which Brodie, but for his early death, might have been able to describe by redefining an operation to include a parameter like heat of combustion as well as weight.[140]

Even in 1907, Edward Divers, a pupil of Williamson, and his obituarist, could write of the 1869 affair: 'but nothing came of it all, and chemists remain not much less divided on the subject now than they were then.'[141] Yet he had to admit that Williamson's structural formulae, in contrast with Brodie's symbols, had turned out to be 'a veritable *calculus of chemical operations.*'[142]

II

The Chemical Calculus of Sir Benjamin Brodie

by

D. M. DALLAS

THE controversy which followed the publication of the 'Calculus of Chemical Operations' by Sir Benjamin Collins Brodie in 1866 illustrates the prevalent dissatisfaction with the atomic theory among chemists and their willingness to consider alternative notations and hypotheses. The story of Brodie's Calculus from its inception and publication, through a respectful but animated reception, to its notoriety and final oblivion, is quite unique in the history of chemistry. In the present discussion my aim has been, principally, to make the main points of the Calculus intelligible, and to do justice to the vision and single-mindedness of its architect.

In his researches prior to the announcement of the Calculus in 1866, Brodie was preoccupied with the problems of allotropy, and the investigation of peroxides which culminated in 1863 with his discovery of the highly dangerous organic peroxides. In a lecture to the Chemical Society in 1864 Brodie discussed what he believed to be the theoretical significance of these peroxides. He began by criticizing Dalton and declared: 'The classification of chemical substances in natural orders ultimately depends on the classification of chemical reactions, or, since the result of every chemical change may be expressed in the form of an equation, on the classification of chemical equations.'[1]

He continued by giving an example of this classification. The substance which would be the same to N_2 as O_2 is to H_2O would be H_2N_2, since

$$2H_3N = 2H_2 + H_2N_2 \quad : \quad 2H_2O = 2H_2 + O_2 \quad \ldots (1)$$

It followed that peroxides were to H_2O what Cl_2 was to HCl, since

$$2H_2O = H_2 + H_2O_2 \quad : \quad 2HCl = H_2 + Cl_2 \quad \ldots (2)$$

Brodie then classified a large number of equations into the forms (1) and (2) in order to show that analogies existed between inorganic electropositive elements, like K and Hg, and organic radicals, like C_2H_5 and C_2H_4 or C_2H_6, but that until recently there had been no analogies in the organic sphere which corresponded to the electronegative elements chlorine, oxygen, nitrogen, etc. However, the organic peroxides provided this missing link, suggested Brodie, because there were parallels between chlorine and the peroxides in the following reactions.

(1) *formation*

$$4HCl + BaO_2 = BaCl_2 + Cl_2 + 2H_2O$$
$$2C_6H_5COCl + BaO_2 = BaCl_2 + C_6H_5CO_2 \cdot O_2CC_6H_5$$

(2) *oxidation*

$$Cl_2 + 2KOH + Mn(OH)_2 = 2KCl + H_2O + MnH_2O_3$$
$$[Mn = 54]$$
$$C_4H_6O_4 + 2KOH + Mn(OH)_2 = 2KC_2H_3O_2 + H_2O + MnH_2O_3$$

Brodie cited other analogous reactions but these two examples are sufficient to show what he meant by classification. He concluded his lecture by suggesting that the analogies between chlorine and the peroxides were so obvious that there was a distinct possibility that oxygen might be discovered in chlorine.

In this theoretical paper Brodie was obviously flushed with the preparative success and important synthesis which he had accomplished, and while we may explain away the wilder suggestions as being due to the excitement and enthusiasm of discovery, there remain some interesting concepts which are worth recording. In his Presidential Address to the British Association in 1864, William Odling makes an obvious reference to Brodie as preparing the first part of the Calculus of Chemical Operations, and he uses the occasion to encourage Brodie with his project.[2] The main point is that Brodie was known to be working on the Calculus in 1864 when the theoretical paper on peroxides was read to the Chemical Society. It is not unlikely that Brodie had made considerable progress with the Calculus already, since, if we may judge from his private papers, the preliminary investigations were quite lengthy. In view of this it is not surprising to find that several ideas in the paper were followed up in the Calculus. The main one was the classification of chlorine with the peroxides leading to the postulate that chlorine was not a simple element. Both chlorine and peroxides play an important part in the arguments used in the Calculus. The other important conception is fundamental: the willingness to classify compounds by equations, and to assume that similar equations were the result of similar compounds rather than of similar reactions.

Brodie's Calculus was published in two long, rather difficult, parts which are summarized in Section I. In Section II there is a description of reactions to its publication; and lastly, in Sections III and IV, I shall attempt to evaluate the Calculus from a more modern chemical and mathematical standpoint, and discuss those aspects of Brodie's philosophy which are relevant to the Calculus.[3]

SECTION I. THE CALCULUS OF CHEMICAL OPERATIONS

Part 1. On the Construction of Chemical Symbols[4]

Brodie starts by expressing dissatisfaction with the atomic nomenclature. The atomic theory does nothing to explain the law of Even Numbers (a rough precursor of the octet rule[5]), or why an arbitrary two-volume system has to be used to express molecular weights. The following system described by Brodie is an attempt to bypass atomism, and is a method of expressing the facts of chemistry by the exact symbols of algebra.

> 'The conditions to be satisfied by such a method are few and simple. It is only necessary that every symbol should be accurately defined; that every arrangement of symbols should be limited by fixed rules of construction, the propriety of which can be demonstrated; and that the symbolic processes employed should lead to results which admit of interpretation.'[6]

The object of the method is to endow chemistry with an exact and rational language by the investigation of the laws of the distribution of weight in chemical changes; the method of analysis is to be operational algebra. In understanding the Calculus, it is imperative to keep two points in mind, (*a*) that the only observable which the Calculus takes into account is weight, and (b) that the symbols stand for *operations* not *weights*.

Brodie's basic unit for the comparison of different substances is a litre, which he calls 'a unit of space.' Operations are performed on the unit of space, and by these operations weights occur; *e.g.*, x_1 might be the symbol of the operation for turning a unit of space into a unit of hydrogen, whose weight would be A_1.

Chemical operations are said to be identical when the results are identical as regards weight. The symbol of identity is $=$. The symbols $+$ and $-$ are used when weights are added to, or taken from, others. o is the symbol of no weight. Brodie says that the use given to these symbols is strictly analogous with that given to them in algebra and arithmetic, whereas in the atomic notation $=$ can be used confusingly as a symbol of either numerical equality or chemical transformation.

The weights of units of space are of two kinds: 'single weights,' and 'compound weights' made up of more that one single weight. If a compound weight is made up of two components, A and B, and the operational symbols for these components are x and y, then the symbol for the compound weight is xy, which is a composite symbol. xy is the symbol of the weight resulting from the successive performance of x and y on a unit of space, and (xy) is the symbol which results from their joint performance. Since they are both identical, $xy = yx = (xy)$.

Brodie then goes on to prove that the operational symbols are distributive, and so there arise four distinctions in operations.

(1) xy is x and y operating successively.

(2) (xy) is x and y operating jointly.

(3) $(x+y)$ is x and y operating collectively.

(4) $x+y$ is x and y operating severally.

Now we come to a crucial section in the Calculus. Since xy is the symbol of a single weight which is composed of the same weight as those of which that group of weights is constituted of which $x+y$ is the symbol,

$$xy = x+y \qquad \ldots (1)$$

This is the *fundamental equation* of the Calculus.

In (1) if $y = 1$, where 1 is the symbol of a unit of space with no weight in it,

$$x = x+1 \qquad \ldots (2)$$

Since $x - x = 0$, then from (2), $0 = 1$.

It can be similarly proved $0 = 1 = 2 = 3 = 4 \ldots = n$.

As we might expect, this was the section which was most discussed by the mathematicians.

Having been inexorably led to this fundamental equation by his preceding definitions, Brodie proceeds to show how the operational analysis applies to chemical reactions. He starts by defining 'simple weights.' These are not compound, have no common component, and cannot be expressed by more than one factor. The symbol of a simple weight is called a *prime factor*, and it is with these prime factors that the Calculus is concerned. The meaning of prime factors will become more clear as concrete examples are chosen.

Brodie's first example is the reaction in which 3 litres of chlorine and 2 litres of ammonia are converted into 6 litres of hydrogen chloride gas and 1 litre of nitrogen.

Let ϕ be the symbol of a unit of chlorine.

ϕ_1 be the symbol of a unit of ammonia.

ϕ_2 be the symbol of a unit of hydrogen chloride.

ϕ_3 be the symbol of a unit of nitrogen.

Then
$$3\phi + 2\phi_1 = 6\phi_2 + \phi_3$$

The empirical result is embodied in the above equation, and all chemical reactions in the vapour state can be expressed in this way. However, we soon find that these equations are not independent, and that they are capable of being derived from one another by addition and subtraction. It is found that a primary system exists, by means of which the relations between the weights of the other units may be expressed. These equations are independent, and they always express relations between the elements and compounds. There can never be a greater number of independent equations than elements without decomposing the elements themselves as, if such an equation were discovered, it would be an equation connecting the symbols of the elements themselves.

Thus the simplest way to get to the prime factors is through equations involving single elements. However, we must make a supposition about one of the elements in order to have a standard against which we can compare the relative weights of the others. This standard, unlike the choice of a litre as the standard volume, involves an assertion as to the actual composition of the standard chosen. Brodie chooses hydrogen, and he makes the assumption that the unit of hydrogen is a simple weight, and that it is undistributed in chemical combination. The operational symbol of the weight of a litre of hydrogen is the prime factor, a.

We find the operational symbol for oxygen as follows. It is experimentally known that 2 units of water may be decomposed into 2 units of hydrogen and 1 unit of oxygen.

Let ϕ be the symbol for a unit of water.

ϕ_1 be the symbol for a unit of hydrogen.

ϕ_2 be the symbol for a unit of oxygen.

Then
$$2\phi = 2\phi_1 + \phi_2$$

Now let
$$\phi = a^m \xi^{m_1}$$
$$\phi_1 = a$$
$$\phi_2 = a^n \xi^{n_1}$$

where a, ξ are prime factors and m, m_1, n, n_1 are positive integers.

Then
$$2a^m \xi^{m_1} = 2a + a^n \xi^{n_1}$$

and from the fundamental equation $x + y = xy$,

$$(a^m \xi^{m_1})^2 = a^2 a^n \xi^{n_1}$$

whence $2m = 2 + n$, and $2m_1 = n_1$

to which is attached the conditions

$w(a) = 1$ (the weight of a litre of hydrogen is 1 gram)

$m + m_1 w(\xi) = 9$ (the weight of a litre of water vapour is 9 grams).

Brodie now lays down three conditions for the solutions of these equations:

   (i) The chemical symbols used must be those which use the least number of prime factors.

  (ii) The prime factors chosen must be the symbols of real weights.

 (iii) The solutions must be integral.

Bearing these conditions in mind, the simplest solution to these equations is,

$$n = 0, \quad m = 1$$
$$n_1 = 2, \quad m_1 = 1$$

Thus the symbol for water is $a\xi$ and the symbol for oxygen is ξ^2, and the relative weights corresponding to the prime factors a and ξ are $w(a) = 1$ and $w(\xi) = 8$.

The equation for the decomposition of water is expressed thus

$$2a\xi = 2a + \xi^2$$

This is an example of how the Calculus establishes the operational symbols for its prime factors. Brodie does a similar analysis for every element, but not every one can be derived as unambiguously as oxygen. He divides the elements into three groups. In the first group, whose symbolic expressions may be found unambiguously, are all the elements which are vapourizable, like oxygen. In the second and third groups are the elements which are not vapourizable, and also those whose compounds are not vapourizable either. Their expression cannot be found unambiguously, and they are graded according to the amount of information available on them. I shall give an example from each section.

After oxygen, Brodie tackles selenium and sulphur to get similar results. Then he goes on to the more thorny problem of chlorine, using as the initial equation the decomposition of hydrogen chloride.

Let $a^m \chi^{m_1}$ be the symbol of a unit of hydrogen chloride and $a^n \chi^{n_1}$ be the symbol of a unit of chlorine.

Then
$$2a^m \chi^{m_1} = a + a^n \chi^{n_1}$$

and
$$(a^m \chi^{m_1})^2 = a a^n \chi^{n_1}$$

whence
$$2m = 1 + n$$
$$2m_1 = n_1$$

and for a minimum solution, $m = 1$, $m_1 = 1$
$$n = 1, \ n_1 = 2$$

Since the density of hydrogen chloride is 18.25, to determine the weight of the simple weight,

$$m + m_1 w(\chi) = 18.25$$
and
$$w(\chi) = 17.25$$

The symbol for hydrogen chloride is therefore $a\chi$, and the symbol for chlorine is $a\chi^2$.

The equation for the decomposition of hydrogen chloride is

$$2a\chi = a + a\chi^2$$

Thus chlorine is the first of a new class of elements whose simple weights can only be expressed by a combination of prime factors, one of which is a. The reason for this, of course, is that this is the first equation Brodie has chosen in which hydrogen is actually distributed. This situation is met with in all elements of odd valency which need an odd number of hydrogen atoms to combine with, as in each case the hydrogen molecule is split.

Exactly similar reasoning leads him to the following symbols.

The symbol for bromine	is $a\beta^2$
iodine	is $a\omega^2$
nitrogen	is $a\nu^2$
phosphorus	is $a^2\phi^4$
arsenic[7]	is $a^2\rho^4$

In each of these cases all the species on either side of the determining equation have been gases, and therefore their volumes have been easily determined. For the rest of the elements Brodie has to deal with equations in which at least one of the elements or compounds is solid, and so the operational formulae are found less equivocally.

In the second group of elements our illustration will be carbon. In the decomposition of methane it is known that the volume of hydrogen produced is twice the volume of the original gas.

Let y be the units of methane decomposed.
Let x be the units of carbon produced.
Let the symbol for methane be $a^m \kappa^{m_1}$.
Let the symbol for carbon be $a^n \kappa^{n_1}$.

Thus $\qquad y a^m \kappa^{m_1} = 2ya + x a^n \kappa^{n_1}$

whence $\qquad (a^m \kappa^{m_1})^y = a^{2y}(a^n \kappa^{n_1})^x$

and $\qquad my = 2y + nx; \quad m_1 y = n_1 x$

The minimum integral solution is $m = 2$, $m_1 = x$
$$n = 0, \quad n_1 = y$$

Thus the symbol for methane is $a^2\kappa^y$ and carbon is κ^y.

The symbol κ^y is applicable to all equations in organic chemistry. It is found that the weight of carbon produced by the decomposition of other organic compounds is always an integral multiple of the weight produced in the decomposition of methane. Thus it is very likely that $y = 1$, as if it was any higher a compound could be formed in which y was distributed. This is not certain but the probability that $y = 1$ is increased the more compounds to which it is found applicable. Similar equations apply to silicon and boron, although boron has an odd valency, and therefore a appears in its symbol. More generally, there are certain empirical rules which may be brought to bear on the indeterminacy of y. These are very important.

Let A be the smallest weight of the element which is formed in the decomposition of a unit of a chemical substance.

Let V be the relative density of the element. It is found that in the case of the elements previously considered that

(i) either $A = V$

(ii) or $A = \dfrac{V}{2}$

(iii) or $A = \dfrac{V}{4}$

(This, of course, correlates with the atomicity of the molecule.) Thus there appears to be an experimental probability in favour of

$$V = A(y = 1), \quad V = 2A(y = 2), \quad V = 4A(y = 4)$$

In the third and last group of the elements are found most of the metals which are all solid, and whose compounds are also solid. Thus Brodie has even less information in the determining equation. However, he ingeniously invokes Dulong and Petit's law, and restates it by saying that the product of A and the specific heat is always constant. Since he cannot use any of the metals to prove this law, as he has no means of determining A, he says that it is empirically proved by studying the elements already dealt with; and he gives a table in which the combination of the specific heats and simple weights is constant for

D

sulphur, selenium, iodine, bromine, phosphorus and arsenic. From this he deduces the Dulong and Petit constant; then from the specific heat of the metal he can obtain a value for A, the simple weight of the metal. Thus, as in the example for carbon, he can say roughly what the indices of the prime factors should be; i.e., the symbol for antimony is either $a\sigma^2$ or $a^2\sigma^4$. Similar arguments apply to bismuth, tin, cadmium and zinc; but when he gets to the very heavy elements he has practically no evidence at all, and he admits that any results must be largely speculation.[8]

Finally Brodie embarks on a defence of his analysis and considers his results. He compares the atomic theory to an abacus, as a tool which might help with problems, but which could easily be discarded. The argument that it is possible to use the atomic notation and yet disbelieve in atoms is firmly rejected. When it is asked what matter is, the only reply is in the interpretation of the symbols by their operations. Chemistry affords no further information on the nature of matter than is given in the interpretation of operations or their results. The Calculus gives the same information as the atomic theory, but unlike the latter it cannot be manipulated at will, for the symbols must obey the rules of the Calculus. 'Such a system is indeed based, in the most absolute sense, upon fact, for it presents only two objects to our consideration, the symbol and the thing signified by the symbol, the object of thought and the object of sense.'[9]

He stresses that the important innovation of the Calculus is that it deals with symbols of operations, and not of quantities. The units of matter must be considered as being made up from their component weights by the successive performance on the unit of space of the operation indicated by the symbols; i.e., a represents the operation of hydrogenizing space, and $a\xi^2$ the successive hydrogenizing and oxygenizing of space to give hydrogen peroxide. However, as well as being a representation of facts, a symbol should also be an instrument for the discovery of facts, and it is by this standard that it must be judged. He continues: 'Now as no symbolic system similar to the present has yet been devised, and as this system cannot be deduced from any existing system, every symbol not only makes an assertion but expresses a discovery as to the chemical properties of that substance symbolized.'[10]

Lastly he summarizes the results of his analysis. The chemical elements may be classed into three groups according to their symbolic expression.

(1) Elements of simple composition, expressed by a single symbol, hydrogen, mercury, and possibly zinc, cadmium, and tin.

(2) Elements composed of two identical simple weights, oxygen, sulphur and selenium.

(3) Complex elements like the halogens $a\chi^2$, or doubled like phosphorus and arsenic $(a\phi^2)^2$ which are composed of a unit of hydrogen and two identical weights; *i.e.*, a combination of the last two groups.

From the fundamental equation $xy = x + y$, we have

$$\xi^2 = \xi + \xi$$
$$a\chi^2 = a + 2\chi$$

'whence we unavoidably have suggested to us the ultimate origin of our actual system of combinations, and as affording an adequate and probable (doubtless we cannot say the only possible or conceivable) explanation of the peculiar phenomena there presented to us, a group of elements ξ, θ, ν, χ, $\ldots$ of the densities indicated by these symbols, and which, though now revealed to us through the numerical properties of chemical equations only as "implicit and dependent existences," we cannot but surmise may some day become, or may in the past have been, "isolated and independent existences." '[11]

However, Brodie ends by equivocating slightly on this visionary concept. These symbols need not be treated in such a way, but they may be used merely as intellectual tools capable of an 'ideal' existence, 'the existence of which as external realities we neither assume nor deny.'

Part 2. On the Analysis of Chemical Events[12]

As we shall see, the publication of the first part of the Calculus in 1866 met with considerable criticism, and Brodie uses the introduction to Part 2 published in 1877 as an opportunity to answer some of the main points raised by his critics.

The first defence he makes is of his choice of the base of the system, hydrogen, as being undistributed. He points out that there are only two possibilities, either the symbol for hydrogen is a or it is a^2. The two are mutually exclusive.[13] He then discusses both of these possibilities in relation to an organic compound of indeterminate formula, and comes to the conclusion that the system based on hydrogen as a predicts the Law of Even Numbers, whereas the other one does not although it is still compatible with the law. Brodie says that in view of this the obvious choice to make is the a hypothesis, as it correlates with the experimental law. The method Brodie uses to substantiate the a hypothesis is largely mathematical and although it is not difficult to follow I shall not attempt to reproduce it here because of its great length and also because it adds nothing new to the analytical method of the Calculus.

Brodie next answers in advance the critics who would say that although the undistributed hypothesis was simpler, yet it leads to the postulate of χ, ν, θ, as real substances. He claims that two arguments render their existence likely. The first is derived from the symbolic representation of the elements like $a\chi^2$, for the possibility of an equation of the form $a\chi^2 = a + 2\chi$ is immediately suggested. However, this argument does not carry much weight, as we are only in a position to make a very small fraction of chemical compounds whose existence is suggested in this way. The second argument is much stronger and more subtle. If one of the elements, say χ, was first predicted and then isolated, there would be little doubt as to the existence of other elements like ν, β, etc. While it is true that χ has not yet been isolated, Brodie gives an example of a situation in which the use of the Calculus would have predicted an element.

He imagines a state called Laputia in which experiments could only be conducted at temperatures between $0°C$ and $300°C$. Under these conditions carbon cannot be isolated. The Laputians would start with the equation that two units of methane are identical with three units of hydrogen and one unit of acetylene. They now have two possibilities, either acetylene can be written as ν^2 or it can be written, as it is at present done in the Calculus, as $\alpha\kappa^2$. Both hypotheses can express all the compounds that the Laputians are likely to meet at these temperatures. However, the second one leads to the Law of Even Numbers, which is empirically verifiable, while the first one does not. Yet the second postulates the existence of carbon, a substance unknown to the Laputians. However, if they adopted the more empirical hypothesis they would find that their predictions as to carbon would be proved correct at higher temperatures.

Brodie goes on to give an important statement of his analytical method. Once it is realized that the information which we have on chemical events is set out in chemical equations, 'a chemical equation becomes a study of transcendent interest, and we are led to consider in a new light the purport and significance of its algebraical properties.'[14] Algebra consists of the analysis of equations which continually yield new truths; the same is empirically true of the chemical Calculus, 'and the most essential and characteristic feature of the Chemical Calculus, by which it is fundamentally discriminated from other modes of considering the science, is that in it we do not, as in the atomic theory, reason by the intervention of material images, but, setting aside all preconceived ideas, we base our arguments upon the equations themselves, and elicit from them, by the application of algebraical processes, the laws and principles which they implicitly contain.'[14]

The fundamental equation introduced in Part I cannot be multiplied in the same way as normal equations, otherwise, *e.g.*

$$xy = x + y$$

multiplying by v

$$vxy = vx + vy \qquad \ldots (2)$$

but

$$vxy = v + x + y$$
$$vx = v + x$$
$$vy = v + y$$

substituting in (2)

$$v = 2v$$

Similarly division is not allowed. Although this is a drawback it is not illogical since in Boolean algebra division is unlawful, and there is nothing in the commutative or distributive laws which implies that multiplication or division is necessarily applicable.

Brodie then goes on to show that there are certain cases where multiplication and division are applicable. These are in chemical equations in which the sum of the numerical coefficients in the equation is equal to zero, *e.g.*

$$2a\chi = a + a\chi^2; \quad 2HCl = H_2 + Cl_2$$

but not in

$$2a^2\nu = 3a + a\nu^2; \quad 2NH_3 = 3H_2 + N_2$$

The former type of equation is called 'normal,' and the latter 'abnormal.' We can 'normalize' abnormal equations by the following technique. Numerical symbols may be added to or subtracted from equations at will, as they are the symbol of no weight in unit space, and the addition of no weight to either side of an equation obviously makes no difference. Hence when the sum of the numerical coefficients is not equal to zero we can make it so merely by the addition of numerical symbols to either side of the equation. In doing this we normalize the equation and render it susceptible to multiplication and division. Examples of normalization are:

Abnormal	*Normal*
$xy = x + y$	$1 + xy = x + y$
$2a^2\nu = 3a + a\nu^2$	$2 + 2a^2\nu = 3a + a\nu^2$
$2a + \xi^2 = 2a\xi$	$2a + \xi^2 = 2a\xi + 1$

Normalization makes the identity in the equation apply not only to weight, but also to space, as there are now the same number of units of space on either side of the equation.

Since Brodie has now established how the equations may be used, the Calculus is ready to be applied as a tool of analytical reasoning, and its use in this field follows the same pattern as in Part 1; namely the precise definition of the terms used, followed by their application.

An equation is the record of a chemical event. Just as simple weights may be included in compound weights, compound events may be made up from the simple events, and the equations will reflect this. In a compound event the equation may be split up into two or more equations which describe the simple events making up the compound one. Brodie analyses a large number of chemical equations, most of them describing substitution reactions. These may be divided into two main groups.

(a) Different Substitutions Occurring Simultaneously

Example: $C_6H_5COCl + KOC_2H_5 = KCl + C_6H_5COOC_2H_5$

$$a^3\kappa^7\xi\chi + a^3\kappa^2\xi\mu = a\chi\mu + a^5\kappa^9\xi^2$$

This may be written

$$a(a^2\kappa^7\xi)\chi + a(a^2\kappa^2\xi)\mu = a\chi\mu + a(a^2\kappa^7\xi)(a^2\kappa^2\xi)$$

factorizing

$$a(a^2\kappa^7\xi - \mu)(\chi - a^2\kappa^2\xi) = 0$$

By this factorization we are informed that in this event a is constant, and that the event occurs in one of two ways, either by the exchange of the weight $a^2\kappa^7\xi$ for μ (C_6H_4CO for K), or of χ for $a^2\kappa^2\xi$ (Cl for OC_2H_4). This hypothesis is relative to this equation alone, and does not involve the assumption that the weights a, $a^2\kappa^7\xi$, $a^2\kappa^2\xi$, χ, are not distributed in another reaction. Where C_6H_5CO and OC_2H_4 appear before the reaction, K and Cl appear after the reaction. Brodie defines the substitution of OC_2H_4 for Cl and C_6H_4CO for K as the 'causes' of the reaction, and he states that when the 'causes' have been determined from the equation, then the chemical event is finally analysed. This means that when the equation factorizes, the event has been analysed and explained.[15]

Equations which factorize immediately include all substitutions which occur simultaneously, like double decomposition, and most syntheses. In most of these cases the events have a number of causes depending on the number of substitutions. When factors like $(\xi - 1)$ occur the result is known as a 'transference,' and these occur in addition reactions.

(*b*) Successive Substitutions

Equations which do not immediately factorize are compound events which have to be broken down into their simple events first. This occurs in the case of substitutions which occur successively, as in di- and tri-substitution.

Example:
$$Cl_2 + 2HI = I_2 + 2HCl$$
$$a\chi^2 + 2a\omega = a\omega^2 + 2a\chi$$

whence
$$a(\chi + \omega - 2)(\chi - \omega) = 0$$

The factor $(\chi + \omega - 2)$ cannot be interpreted as it stands. However, we can easily convert the equation into an interpretable form by resolving this factor. Thus the equation becomes

$$a(\chi - 1)(\chi - \omega) + a(\omega - 1)(\chi - \omega) = 0$$

Brodie had previously given a mathematical proof, which is too long for inclusion here, that the product of two or more brackets multiplied together must equal zero. Thus each term in the above equation is equal to zero and the event is aggregated of two simple events.

$$a(\chi - 1)(\chi - \omega) = 0$$
$$a(\omega - 1)(\chi - \omega) = 0$$

Since these equations have a common factor $(\chi - \omega)$, the events may be referred to a common cause, the substitution of ω for χ. Also each part has an alternative cause, the transference of χ or ω. The constituent equations are

$$a\chi^2 + a\omega = a\chi + a\omega\chi$$
$$a\omega\chi + a\omega = a\omega^2 + a\chi$$

The intermediate stage here is the formation of iodine monochloride, which has been isolated in kinetic studies of the reaction,[16] and this reaction is made up of two successive substitutions of Cl for I.

The rest of this section of Part 2 follows this pattern and discusses di- and tri-substitution, where it is generally possible to isolate the intermediate steps.

The last section of the Calculus is the most general in either Part, and is intended to explain chemical phenomena by the analysis of chemical equations. It is largely mathematical, and because of this, and also because it adds nothing more to the methods of analysis, I shall only summarize it briefly.

Brodie starts by saying that the symbol $(x-a)$ which occurs among the factors of a chemical equation is the symbol of an operation of which the result is the exchange of a 'bit of matter' resulting from the operation 'a' for a 'bit of matter' resulting from the operation 'x'. It is not to be interpreted as the symbol of any weight, as there is no external reality corresponding to the difference $w(x) - w(a)$. Nor is the exchange a simple one:

> 'on the contrary, when the unit of hydrochloric acid $a\chi$ passes into the unit of water $a\xi$ by the process of which the final result is the substitution in that unit of ξ for χ, that unit must be regarded as passing by a process of continual change through every value intermediate between $a\chi$ and $a\xi$, an assumption in perfect accordance with what we know of the gradual character of chemical changes.'[17]

The relations which exist between 'bits of matter' are perceived in the factorization and aggregation of their chemical equations. After a long mathematical section, which includes the use of Taylor's theorem, Brodie arrives at the following general definition of a chemical equation.

> 'If in any chemical equation $u = 0$ the prime factors by which the equation is expressed be severally and simultaneously put equal to 1 (which is the only numerical value of chemical symbols), that equation vanishes, and also if we differentiate the equation once in regard to any one (and every one) of these factors, and on the result of that differentiation put all the prime factors severally and simultaneously equal to 1, that differential coefficient also vanishes.'[18]

Every chemical equation may be regarded as a member of the general system of the form

$$f(a, \chi, \nu, \mu, \ldots) = 0$$

Thus every such equation vanishes when the prime factors a, χ, ν, etc. are severally and simultaneously put equal to 1. Every chemical equation may be considered to occur by the transferences of the simple weights $w(a)$, $w(\chi)$ etc., and chemical equations can be resolved into a set of constituent simple events, which are the only set of causes to which these phenomena can be referred. All brackets of the form $(x-a)$ or $(xy-ab)$ may be expressed by means of the more simple brackets $(x-1)$ — $(a-1)$ etc., and the transference between simple weights is the final explanation of chemical phenomena.

On this triumphant note the Calculus ends.

SECTION II. PUBLISHED REACTIONS TO THE CALCULUS

Reactions to Part I[19]

When the first part of the Calculus was published in 1866 it aroused general interest. Brodie was invited to give a lecture to the Chemical Society to explain some of the more difficult points.[20] His lecture, entitled 'Ideal Chemistry,'[21] was given to a joint meeting of the Chemical Society and the Royal Society in June 1867; it was very well attended, and, in the discussion which followed, Williamson, Frankland, Maxwell, Stokes, Wanklyn, Odling, Brayley, and Carey Foster all spoke. In many ways the lecture was unsatisfactory as an exposition of the Calculus, but fortunately this did not hinder the later discussion, as obviously most of the audience had taken the trouble to read the first part of the Calculus.

Chemical News devoted almost a whole issue to the lecture, entitling it 'The Chemistry of the Future.'[22] Brodie gave his reasons for being dissatisfied with the atomic theory, dwelt on the nature of the symbols used in the Calculus, with examples drawn from vector geometry, and said that the operational symbols represented the 'packing' of matter into space in the formation of an element or compound. When he dealt with the 'ideal' elements he suggested that it was possible that χ, ν, θ etc., existed long ago in the earth when the temperature was much higher. As the earth cooled down they combined with a to form the very stable combinations $a\chi^2$, $a^2\nu$ etc. He believed this might be confirmed by spectroscopic work on nitrogen.

Williamson, chairman at the meeting, thanked Brodie for the lecture, and added that although he could not fully appreciate all the expressions used, he was sure the Calculus would 'inaugurate an exceedingly important era in chemical language and notation.' Edward Frankland, the first speaker from the floor, admitted that he did not believe in atoms and that there was widespread dissatisfaction with chemical formulae, but before praising the Calculus for its novelty and imagination, and saying that it was an important landmark in chemical thought, he made two criticisms of the symbols. (1) That the concept of force was absent from both the atomic notation and the Calculus. (2) That the predictive value of the Calculus was questionable. He suggested that it was absolutely certain that the hydrogen present in sulphuric acid could be removed in two pieces, whereas that in nitric acid could only be removed in one. This fact was included in the atomic formulae H_2SO_4 and HNO_3, but not in $a\theta\xi^4$ and $a\nu\xi^3$. Little comment need be made about the first criticism as even the present notation has not dared to tackle the problem of interatomic forces. The second criticism was answered by Foster, so I shall postpone discussion of it until I deal with his remarks.

The next speaker was the physicist James Clerk Maxwell, a specially invited guest. He said that on entering the room he was shocked to find on the blackboard that space was a chemical substance and that hydrogen and mercury were operations. However, he was now reassured that 'the present [Calculus] seemed to be an endeavour to cause the symbols of chemical substances to act in formulae according to their own laws.' He noted the similarity between the Calculus and Boole's algebra,[23] and he grasped that a is not hydrogen, but 'make hydrogen.' However, he said that to get double the volume in a litre, to obtain a^2, either the temperature or the pressure had to be altered, thus invalidating the symbols which had to be used at N.T.P. by definition. In order to get a^2, two volumes would have to be compressed into one at the same temperature and pressure, a process which is unknown.

Maxwell believed that the kinetic theory of gases supported the existence of atoms and also led to the belief that in a litre of gas at N.T.P. there are the same number of molecules or atoms, whatever the gas, and that this assumption was also implied in the Calculus. The kinetic theory of Clausius was now on probation, but the next step, in the near future, would be to find out the number of molecules in a litre at N.T.P.; then there would be a new unit of weight, the molecule.

In his first objection Maxwell misunderstood the operational nature of the symbols, for he supposed that they symbolized physical operations, not chemical ones. Not all operations can be performed, only those which occur experimentally in reactions. The operation a^2 occurs in the following reaction:

$$CO + 2H_2 = CH_3OH$$
$$\kappa\xi + 2a = \kappa a^2\xi$$

But the operation a^2 is performed on carbon monoxide under certain conditions only, and only under these conditions will the use of a^2 be lawful. Maxwell may have been confusing this with $2a$, which is two volumes of hydrogen at N.T.P. His second point, that Avogadro's hypothesis is a concealed premise, is certainly valid, although it is a reformulation of the Calculus in atomic terms, and is not necessarily a criticism. His prophecy about the molecule was remarkably prescient.

Another physicist, George Stokes, briefly commended the way in which the Calculus expressed compositions using all the existing empirical knowledge, but not assuming anything else. However, he said that the anomalies of nitric oxide and nitrogen dioxide must be adequately explained before the Calculus could be adopted in favour of the Laurent-Gerhardt system.

Wanklyn then commented that Brodie's Calculus was essentially a one-volume system in contrast to the Laurent-Gerhardt two-volume system. This rather superficial objection ignored the reasons for adopting undistributed hydrogen as the base, and also the fact that Brodie's method of classification on this base not only determined the relative values of the simple weights in relation to that of hydrogen, but also determined the actual constitution of the elements themselves. It is because a is the symbol for hydrogen, and because this cannot be split, that the symbol for chlorine is $a\chi^2$.

Odling then confided to the company that Williamson had just remarked to him that it was obvious that Frankland had never believed in atoms or he would never have taken such liberties with them in his textbook, *Lecture Notes for Chemistry Students*. He praised the Calculus and thought that its main merits were that it was a one-volume system without any fractions, and also that in it expressions were brought into immediate relations with facts without the intervention of hypothetical atoms.

On a more practical note Brayley suggested that the most important point about the Calculus was the possibility of finding hydrogen in the haloid elements. Foster endorsed this, and noted that chlorine was generally believed to have been an oxide of murium before its elementary character had been demonstrated by Davy. He went on to answer Frankland's criticism[24] about sulphuric and nitric acids by saying that the basicity of an acid must be judged with reference to the whole formula, not just to the α part. The formula for water is $\alpha\xi$ and the formula for hydrogen chloride is $\alpha\chi$. Yet hydrogen can be removed from the water by two stages and from the HCl by only one. By looking at the whole formula we see that the χ in $\alpha\chi$ renders the adjacent α undistributible, while the ξ in $\alpha\xi$ does not, and this applies generally to these elements. In the case of nitric acid, $\alpha\nu\xi^3$, the α is undistributed due to the adjacent ν, while for the sulphuric acid, $\alpha\theta\xi^4$, the θ has no effect on the adjacent elements. This explanation was corroborated by Brodie.[25]

In spite of these criticisms the tone of all the speakers was respectful, and at times flattering. Some of the praise was mere convention, as many of the speakers attacked Brodie bitterly in later papers and lectures. However, it is certain that much of the admiration was due to a genuine desire to rethink the problems of notation and the atomic theory.

A fortnight after Brodie's lecture Williamson read a short paper on the Calculus to the Royal Society.[26] As is shown in Brodie's private correspondence,[27] Williamson took trouble to understand the Calculus, and some of his criticisms are very telling. His first point was that it is not always possible to obtain the operational formula for a substance through its reaction in the vapour phase. Among the compounds whose relative weights and formulae are given in the Calculus are S, SO_2, SO_3, H_2S, H_2SO_3, H_2SO_4, and $H_2S_2O_7$. The formula for the element was obtained from the vapour density of the gas, and the vapour densities of all the above sulphur compounds are given in a table.[28] However, H_2SO_3, H_2SO_4, and $H_2S_2O_7$ all dissociate on heating, so the vapour densities given in the table are not the experimental ones. How then did Brodie arrive at their formulae? It was certainly not through the vapour density, suggested Williamson. There are many other examples of compounds which dissociate or decompose on heating, and whose formulae may not be determined in this way. Thus vapour densities are not a universal method of obtaining molecular formulae, an assumption which Williamson said is implicit in Brodie's Calculus.

Williamson then raised the rather trivial objection that it is inconvenient to define the units of matter with reference to the litre, as this means that one has to remember the weights as a fraction of $11 \cdot 4$. But this, of course, could easily be avoided if the weights were considered as multiples of the simple weight of hydrogen. He noticed that all elements of odd valency contain hydrogen, and he thought that if this nomenclature was to be avoided then it should be extended to elements of even valency, so that the synthesis of water would be:

$$2a + a^2 \xi^2 = 2a^2 \xi$$

This ignores one of the basic principles of the Calculus, clearly stated by Brodie in Part I, namely that the representation of the compounds should be that which is necessary and sufficient only to represent the compound in its equations. While $a^2 \xi^2$ is sufficient to represent oxygen in all its reactions it is not necessary, and only ξ^2 fulfils all the conditions.

However, if we look at this simplicity principle more closely we find that its foundations are dubious. In the original equations which determine the number of prime factors in the elements there are more unknowns than equations. In order to get single valued results Brodie insists that the symbols should consist of the least number of prime factors. This is a short cut to obtain a single value for the prime factor, and it is never theoretically justified. In many ways it is similar to the 'simplicity rule' of Dalton, namely that when two elements form only one compound then the formula will be the simplest; *i.e.*, *AB*. In both cases these chemists tried to disguise a chemically doubtful step by an appeal to simplicity.

Williamson concluded by pointing out another weakness in

the rules for determining the operational formulae for an element or compound. The condition that the solution should be an *integral* number of prime factors was completely unjustified unless one accepted the atomic theory, which can provide a satisfactory reason for integral values; *i.e.*, since atoms cannot be split there must be an integral number of atoms in a molecule. This was certainly a most pertinent criticism, and there is some evidence from Brodie's private papers that he saw this problem and tried to find a way round it.[29]

The discussion after this lecture was not reported by the *Chemical News*, but *Laboratory*[30] carried a report of the defence of the Calculus made by Odling, who dealt with Williamson's points in turn. He started by saying that the method of obtaining formulae by vapour densities is convenient because it compares matter in its simplest form. When gas volumes of different substances are compared it is found that there are certain special relations of heat, weight, etc., and that non-volatile compounds display these relationships as well. Thus when a substance dissociates on heating the formula may be obtained indirectly through these relations, rather than through the vapour density.

Odling argued that Williamson's formula for oxygen violates Occam's razor. This is true, but he omitted to say that Occam's razor is only a universal principle in logic, not in chemistry. He answered the claim that Brodie could not reason without the atomic theory by saying that the Calculus is independent of the atomic theory, but not necessarily incompatible with it. This was a glib answer rather than an explanatory one, and the fact that the indices of the prime factors must be integral remained unexplained.

In a last ingenious argument Odling said that there was empirical evidence for the indivisibility of the hydrogen molecule. He noticed that, in multivalent elements, hydrogen is only added on in multiples of 2 (using the atomic notation). For an element X, hydrogen is added on to give XH_2, XH_4, XH_6, while oxygen is added XO, XO_2, XO_3. Therefore hydrogen is not dissociated, while oxygen is, and the undistributed elements are either single, like α, or treble like $\alpha\chi^2$, while distributed ones are double like ξ^2. This, of course, is largely true, although Odling omits to mention that chlorine can be added singly.

However, the reasons for this (odd and even valency) could hardly have been obvious to Odling!

Laboratory printed a long and interesting correspondence on the subject of the Calculus in which a number of distinguished chemists and philosophers took part. Its first communication (after the report on Brodie's lecture)[31] was from Davey, and included part of a speech which he had been unable to deliver after the lecture. He quoted Brodie as saying that the notation of the Calculus could not be deduced from any other system. Davey sought to refute this, and gave certain rules for writing out the new symbolic notation without the aid of the Calculus.

For the elements:

(1) Let a represent hydrogen.

(2) Let the initial letter or other letter in the Greek name of the element be the characteristic in the new symbol.

(3) Write a 2 as index in the characteristic letter (except for Hg, Cd, P, As).

(4) When the element can combine with an odd number of units of hydrogen, prefix a to the symbol.

For compounds:

(5) Substitute for each of the elementary symbols in the old notation the corresponding new Greek symbol, and multiply its indices by the coefficient of the old symbol.

(6) Add the indices of all like symbols together and then divide by two.

He gave the examples of chlorine and hydrogen chloride, and closed with the remark: 'The chief points of difference between this new notation and the one in daily use are the substitution of Greek for Roman letters and the implied assumption that one litre of hydrochloric acid contains a litre of hydrogen.'[32] Davey's rules seem to work on an *ad hoc* basis, but he missed the point when he claimed to have derived the Calculus from the atomic notation. The substitution of *ad hoc* rules is in no sense a derivation. Perhaps he would not have written this if he had seen the second part of the Calculus, and had realized how much it differed from the atomic conception.

The next correspondent was Stanley Jevons, the mathematician and philosopher.[33] In a public exchange of letters with Brodie some extremely important criticisms of the Calculus emerged, which struck at the root of the mathematical formulation of the Calculus.[34] In the first letter Jevons claimed that there was an inconsistency in the mathematical equations of the Calculus, and, by multiplying both sides of the fundamental equation, he arrived at largely the same inconsistency which Brodie pointed out in his discussion of the fundamental equation in Part 2.[35]

In the next issue,[36] Brodie replied that he had taken care to say in Part 1 that multiplication and division could only be undertaken in circumstances to be explained later. As the fundamental equation was not one of those equations which could be multiplied the inconsistency would never arise.

However, Brodie was not quite accurate in his defence, for as Jevons was quick to point out,[37] multiplication was not necessary to lead to this contradiction since it could be reached merely by substitution—a process which was lawful in the Calculus. In the basic equation

$$x(y_1 + y_2) = xy_1 + xy_2 \qquad \ldots (1)$$

substitute x for y_1 and y_2.

Then
$$x(x + x) = xx + xx \qquad \ldots (2)$$

but
$$xx = x + x \qquad \ldots (3)$$

substituting this in (2)

$$xxx = xx + xx$$

and from (3)

$$x + x + x = x + x + x + x$$

The contradiction arises, as Jevons realized, because equations (3) and (2) are incompatible. This basic mathematical difficulty in the Calculus was noticed by Crum Brown and other mathematicians,[38] but Brodie never answered this criticism. The solution to the problem will be discussed later.

The latter half of Jevons's second letter deals with a slightly different point. He noted that Williamson had said that the application of algebra to chemistry was of 'incalculable importance.'[39] Jevons could not agree, and he denied that the symbol

E

xy involved multiplication any more than the symbol HCl. He thought that Brodie had tried to get round this by invoking operations:

> 'We begin with the unit of empty space, 1; we operate upon it with x to get $x \cdot 1$, and the weight x; then we operate again and get the weight $y + x$. I deny that the second operation is the same as the first. *To add further weight* is not a repetition of the operation *to turn space into weight*.'[40]

He returned to Gregory's original paper to which Brodie had referred in a footnote in Part 1, and he compared the symbols;[41]

Gregory's symbols	x	$a(x)$	$b(a(x))$
Meaning	point	line	parallelogram
Brodie's symbols	1	$x \cdot 1$	$y \cdot x \cdot 1$
Brodie's meaning	space	weight	increased weight
True meaning	space	weight	inconceivable

In conclusion Jevons said that Brodie should not multiply or divide, but merely add or subtract, and he also denied Brodie's contentions that (a) 'a true chemical calculus may be developed, in which we are enabled to reason by the agency of the same algebraic processes through which reasoning is conducted in arithmetical algebra';[42] (b) xy is 'the symbol of a compound weight, an exact interpretation in harmony with symbolic analogies.'[43]

Although Brodie did not meet this objection, an obvious response is that multiplication of the prime factors is not meant to be in any way analogous to the atomic conception of HCl, nor to the mode of production of the compound. The algebraic form of the Calculus is meant to be a tool for discovery and classification, and there is no more contradiction in applying algebra to chemistry than in applying it to logic, which Boole had done successfully. The test of the method is whether it works in practice, not in *a priori* analysis of whether multiplication is analogous to combination.

The argument about the meaning of symbols can be met as follows; we can say in each case we really operate on space, but that in combination we do so by means of two operations (in binary combinations), first operating with one element, and then with the other. In this case the result is weight for both the element and the compound. Probably Jevons was worried about the introduction of the unit of space into the Calculus, as this was an unusual concept in chemical thinking. However, although unusual, it is not necessarily wrong, and in many ways is merely a convenient operand.

The last communication on the subject of the Calculus printed in *Laboratory* was from Kekulé[44] who noted that the Calculus involved the classification of the elements into three groups, simple, binary, and ternary.[45] He criticized the Calculus on three grounds. (1) He noted that if chlorine or nitrogen had been adopted as the base of the Calculus these elements would not have contained hydrogen, and in this case hydrogen would have been a compound element. It was clear to Kekulé 'that a system of symbols cannot be admitted as a true representation of actual facts, unless its results are independent of the particular member of the system which has been taken as a starting point for the constitution of the whole.'[46] (2) Even if hydrogen were accepted as the base of the system, what proof had Brodie that hydrogen was an element? (3) The operation for hydrogenizing was a, why not a^2? 'The hypothesis $H = a$ is said to be the simplest that could be adopted; but it may be laid down as a general rule that, in selecting from a number of different hypotheses the one which is most probable on the ground of simplicity, it is necessary to look, not only at the relative simplicity of the hypothesis itself, but to the more or less simple character of the consequences which follow it.' He concluded by quoting Dalton: 'a substance, until it is decomposed, must be regarded, according to the just logic of chemistry, as an elementary substance.'

It is clear that Kekulé had taken time and trouble to understand the Calculus, and all his criticisms are searching. I shall deal with the first part of (1) in a later discussion of a paper by Wanklyn and Davey which argued that hydrogen was the only element that could have been used as the base for the Calculus. In the second part of (1), Kekulé realized that the Calculus is not simply a one-volume system, but that the base determines the constitution of the other elements. It is not necessarily true that no system can be admitted unless the results are independent of the starting point, but, if such a system is to be used, the starting point must be one about which there can be no confusion or doubt. It is in this respect that the Calculus is deficient, as Kekulé made plain in objection (2), to which no adequate reply can be made. Brodie had no criteria for determining simple weights other than through equations, and there is no such determining equation for hydrogen.

The first part of (3) was explained by Brodie in Part 2 which had not been printed when Kekulé wrote his letter. The passage quoted from (3) is a very valid criticism of the use of simplicity criteria at any time, and it is especially relevant to the Calculus. The hypothesis that $H = a$, although the simplest, does not lead to the simplest consequences.

The Calculus came under further scrutiny at the British Association meeting in Dundee in 1867. The President of the Chemistry Section, Thomas Anderson, devoted almost his entire address to the subject. He thought that the atomic theory could no longer explain the accumulating facts of chemistry, and that phrases like catalysis, allotropy, etc., really explain nothing at all. The time had come either to abandon Dalton or to radically modify his theory. After summarizing the Calculus, he spoke of the possibility that some of the elements might be compounds. He could not 'imagine that much difficulty will be experienced by anyone in admitting the possibility of this, for I apprehend there is no chemist who imagines those bodies which we call elements to be the ultimate constituents of matter, or who doubts that the time, though still far distant, will come when they may be resolved into simpler substances.'[47] It is clear that Anderson was singularly open-minded on the subject of atoms and the atomic theory.

In his balanced discussion of the Calculus he noted that, if the $H = a^2$ hypothesis had been used, then the compound elements would not have arisen. He objected to the consideration of space in chemistry, as he believed that the real subject of chemical enquiry was the unit of matter—a criticism which is more relevant to Part 2 where the equations are made spatially accurate in order to make them factorize. He thought that some kind of molecular hypothesis was indispensable, as there must be a connection between chemical and physical units of matter.

That he was aware that chemical theories would also have to fit physics is the more notable because this attitude was absent in many chemists of that period. Had there been a closer liaison between physics and chemistry, there might have been less scepticism towards the atomic theory.

Another speaker at Dundee with a particular interest in the Calculus was Crum Brown, who had himself almost simultaneously published a paper on some applications of mathematics to chemistry.[48] He read a report on the Calculus which was followed by a lively discussion.[49] In this paper he made three objections to the Calculus:

(1) That the distributive law is unnecessary, and leads to anomalies on multiplying both sides of the fundamental equation.

(2) That there is no evidence that hydrogen is undistributed, and that this assumption leads to inconvenient formulae for the triad elements.

(3) That a notation similar to that of Brodie might be deduced on the reasonable assumption that bodies hitherto undecomposed should not be represented as compound. In this way the ordinary chemical symbols might be used in a functional way as well as in an atomic sense.

Crum Brown had already published a longer critique of the Calculus earlier in 1867.[50] In this he started by saying that although physical researches lead to a molecular interpretation of matter, the chemist is indifferent as to whether his symbols represent atoms, molecules, or units. (Fortunately chemists were perhaps not so indifferent as Crum Brown imagined.) His major criticisms fall under the following headings.

(1) The distributive law. Here he made the same point as Jevons that there is a contradiction between the distributive law and the identity of addition and multiplication.

(2) Chemical symbols. In the Calculus $2x$ is used to mean two litres of x. If instead it was used to mean 1 unit of weight put into 2 litres of space then the anomalies to the Law of Even Numbers like the oxides of nitrogen could be suitably explained. Unfortunately, this is equivalent to asserting that hydrogen, and every other element, can be distributed. However, it again

poses the problem of what exactly 2*x* represents, a problem to which we shall return.

(3) Brodie's assumptions. In order to get integral weights Brodie had to assume that there are no negative or fractional indices. These assumptions were common to the atomic theory, and the only new assumption he made was that hydrogen is undistributed. Crum Brown followed this with a set of rules for transposing from Brodie's notation to Dalton's. These are very similar to Davey's rules, but again they ignore the operational nature of the Calculus.

(4) Comparison. Lastly, Crum Brown compared the two notations in terms of flexibility, usefulness and reasonableness, and he found the atomic notation better on each account. (*a*) He said that the atomic notation is more reasonable in its foundation as we have no means of splitting the elements at present. Following Kekulé, he thought that if hydrogen were the only element to consider, then Brodie's system would probably be the best; but taking all the other elements into consideration the atomic one was simplest. (*b*) He also claimed that the atomic system was more flexible. If chlorine really was murium oxide (as he thought Brodie's researches into the organic peroxides might well prove[1]), then this could easily be accommodated into the atomic notation, but if hydrogen proved to be a compound element then the Calculus could not be modified to accommodate this. I think that this is being a bit unfair, as if chlorine was found to be a compound element it would have been a triumph of prediction for Brodie. (*c*) He made the important empirical point that if hydrogen is seen in the formula of a compound, then on combustion it always gives water; but if a is seen in the formula, combustion with oxygen need not produce water. This point is similar to that raised by Frankland earlier, and can be dealt with in the same way, namely that the combustion products may be predicted if reference is made to the whole of the formula, not just the a part. (*d*) Brodie must be very careful to distinguish between what can be done in terms of operations, namely a, and what cannot, *e.g.*, χ. Crum Brown regarded the division between the two as very arbitrary, and entirely unexplained. This can be countered by saying that the symbols are merely tools of thought, and whether

they can be performed under normal experimental conditions is a matter for empirical investigation.

In the same issue of the *Philosophical Magazine*, Wanklyn and Davey published a paper entitled 'Observations on Sir Benjamin Brodie's "Ideal Chemistry" '.[51] Their tone was highly critical, and they ridiculed Brodie's attack on the conventional use of mathematical symbols.

'On page 795 we are startled by the following statement, "No uniform meaning has hitherto been attached to the symbols + and − in chemistry, notwithstanding their constant use. The prevalent opinion seems to be in favour of the use of the symbol + as the symbol of mechanical mixture. . . . A similar uncertainty prevails in the use of the symbol of identity. The symbol = is sometimes employed in chemistry as the symbol of numerical equality, at other times as a symbol of chemical transmutation."

'These extracts afford a not unfair sample of the kind of reasoning to be met with in this paper. We reply to these (although at the risk of being considered tedious), that although the one side of an equation may be the other side which has undergone the transmutation, yet it is not the = which expresses the transmutation, but the different arrangement of the symbols expresses the transmutation. And similarly the +, although it is often written between things in mechanical mixture, does not express such a mixture, but is always used by the chemist in its strictly algebraical sense.'[52]

The writers went on to notice that if a^2 had been used as the base then the new notation would have been the old one translated into Greek, and chlorine need not be considered as a compound element. Brodie was to be 'congratulated' on taking a as the base.

'Suppose, in an evil hour, he had taken ξ as the modulus, . . . Mark the consequences Sir B. Brodie has escaped. The litre of oxygen ξ is the least quantity of oxygen which can exist, and if a litre contains any oxygen at all, it must contain 1·430 gm. of oxygen. Unfortunately, a litre of steam weighs only 0·805 gm. Would not the modulus ξ lead us straight to phlogiston, which, as we all know, is blessed with a negative weight, and which would figure as a in steam with a negative weight of 0·625 gm.

'Chlorine a compound, phlogiston—Behold the results of the Chemical Calculus.'[53]

Wanklyn and Davey's two major criticisms, about the use of $+$ and $-$, and the concept of negative weight, are most pertinent. In chemical equations the symbols $+$ and $-$ are used in the same sense as in arithmetic, and no confusion need arise. Confusion arises only when observation-statements are attached to these mathematical symbols and, consequently, the symbols are identified as being merely the observations. Chemical equations are a convenient way of representing the facts of chemistry only because of the empirical evidence that matter is neither created nor destroyed in a chemical reaction. Matter is represented by chemical symbols and the equality of weight is conveniently represented in mathematics by an equation. This is why we write

$$Zn + H_2SO_4 = ZnSO_4 + H_2$$

The following equation, $Zn + H_2SO_4 = ZnSO_4$, is unlawful, because one of the conventions involved in writing an equation is that everything which occurs on the left-hand side must reappear on the right-hand side. However, we could write another equation,

$$Zn + H_2SO_4 = ZnHSO_4 + H$$

This equation is mathematically lawful, but may be chemically untrue. Chemical equations obey the additional criterion that the reaction products must be discriminable. The only way this can be done is by observing the transformations involved when the reactants on the left-hand side of the equation become the products on the right-hand side.

Thus it was Brodie who was confusing the role played by '$=$' in a chemical equation. The use of '$=$' is mathematically consistent, but the way in which the equation is verified is by observing the transmutation, so that if the equation expresses a true result the equal sign expresses the transmutation as well.

Wanklyn and Davey's second objection is that hydrogen is the only undistributed element that could be chosen as the base of the system. Brodie never revealed this publicly, although he admitted it in his private papers,[54] and explained it as follows. If chlorine had been assumed to be undistributed, then the symbols would have been

$$Cl_2 \quad a' \qquad HCl \quad a'\chi' \qquad H_2 \quad a\chi'^2$$

i.e., on going from chlorine to hydrogen chloride the operation χ' is performed. But as the simple weight of hydrogen chloride is less than that of chlorine, this means that the operation χ' produces negative weight. As this is contrary to the conception of an operation as bestowing weight on space, there can be no such operation. Thus only the least dense element can be used as the base of the Calculus as all operations on this element are weight producing, and therefore allowed.

Williamson's lecture to the Chemical Society in 1869 was a measure of the widespread interest in alternatives to the atomic theory, and it is to the credit of the Calculus that most of the audience remained sceptical at its conclusion.[55] At another meeting which was held to discuss the points raised by Williamson, Brodie made a poor defence of the Calculus, and the only new point which he mentioned was that it was the laws of gaseous combination which led to integral indices being used for prime factors. However, Gay Lussac's law could only be used as a guide, as the ratios of the volumes of reacting gases is never exactly an integral number.[56]

In 1872 Brodie published an elegant paper on the constitution of ozone.[57] After much painstaking and detailed work he had established beyond doubt that the formula for ozone was ξ^3. In this paper he used the notation of the Calculus, and he suggested that the allotrope ξ^3 proved the existence of the triad class of elements, and therefore that $a\chi^2$ becomes much more probable. The formula for hydrogen peroxide is $a\xi^2$, and if ξ is substituted for a then ozone is obtained. This analogy is reinforced by the remarkable similarity in oxidizing properties between ozone and the peroxides. In a similar manner, from $a\xi^2$, by the substitution of χ for ξ we reach $a\chi^2$, which is chlorine. This also has properties closely analogous to the peroxides, as had been pointed out by Brodie in an earlier paper.[1] The remarkable similarity in oxidizing properties between these elements and compounds seemed to Brodie to be an empirical vindication of the Calculus.

Reactions to Part 2

Probably because of illness, Part 2 of the Calculus was not published until 1877, eleven years after Part 1. There was scarcely any controversy over its publication, and it was largely ignored. *Laboratory* had long since ceased to be active, and *Chemical News* and *Nature* did not even mention it; while among individual chemists, many had forgotten about the techniques of the Calculus, or only had a very dim recollection of them. Furthermore, in the intervening years, van't Hoff and le Bel had published their papers on the stereochemistry of carbon, while the concept of valency had given a simple explanation of the Law of Even Numbers on which so much of Brodie's thinking depended.

Brodie was not deterred by the cool reception and, almost simultaneously with the production of Part 2, he produced a paper 'On the relative "Facility of Production" of chemical compounds,'[58] which was an extremely ingenious defence of the Calculus based on empirical evidence from the hydrocarbons. He started by saying that there were very few chemical substances which actually existed out of the possible combinations and permutations of all the elements. His aim was to show that the probability of the existence of any compound, from a combination of its elements, depended on unalterable mathematical laws. The 'facility' for doing a is the same as that for doing ξ, but this does not apply to more than one prime factor where different permutations of the symbols give different 'facilities of production' and therefore different probabilities of existence. There is only one way to make ξ and there is only one way to make ξ^2, as it does not matter in which order the operations ξ occur. However, in a compound like $a\xi$, either a or ξ occurs first.[59] The end result is the same, as $a\xi = \xi a$, but the 'facility of production' of $a\xi$ is twice that of a^2 or ξ^2, as there are two ways of making $a\xi$, depending on which operation comes first.

Thus the 'facility of production' of the following compounds is in the order of possible permutations of their symbols; viz, the sequence

$$?a^2 \qquad H_2O \; a\xi \qquad H_2O_2 \; a\xi^2 \qquad O_3 \; \xi^3$$
$$\text{I} \qquad\qquad 2 \qquad\qquad\quad 3 \qquad\qquad\quad \text{I}$$

The compound or element with the greatest 'facility of production' (which is best thought of as probability of being isolated) has the most chance of being prepared, and this was borne out in that ozone had been only recently prepared, and a^2 had not been isolated.

Turning to the hydrocarbons, Brodie compared the 'facility of production' of a number of compounds; e.g., $a^4\kappa^5$ and $a^3\kappa^6$. He stressed that only compounds with the same number of prime factors, as above (9) could be compared. There could be no such comparison between $a^4\kappa^5$ and $a^3\kappa^2$. He then found that the greatest 'facility of production' should occur for compounds with about the same number of prime factors a and κ because, for example, the number of permutations is greater for $a^4\kappa^5$ than for $a^3\kappa^6$. Thus for different numbers of prime factors the most probable compounds are, for example, $a^2\kappa^2$ C_2H_4, $a^3\kappa^3$ C_3H_6, $a^4\kappa^4$ C_4H_8. To his great delight, he found that most of these compounds had indeed been prepared, whereas ones with a low 'facility of production' like $a^2\kappa^4$ C_4H_4, had not. He illustrated this in an elaborate table showing which compounds had been prepared and which not, and showing that, on the whole, compounds with a high 'facility of production' had been isolated, while those without this were not known. The Calculus again appeared to have predicted an important principle.

Although there does not seem to have been any contemporary criticism of Brodie's conclusions, the main objections are:

(1) He cannot explain any of the aromatic, or cyclic compounds.

(2) The phrase 'facility of production' ignores any of the considerations of thermodynamics, thermochemistry, reaction path, and many other physical considerations.

(3) Brodie's conclusions only work because the predicted compounds included the alkanes and alkenes. This was pure

coincidence, and had he used the α^2 hypothesis there would have been no correlation between the predicted and the isolated compounds.

(4) Brodie cannot give 'facilities of production' for different isomers. Indeed, in the table there is only one recorded compound for a formula like $\alpha^4\kappa^4$ (C_4H_8) which may have several structural isomers.

In his private papers there is evidence that Brodie looked for similar relations in the compounds of carbon, nitrogen, oxygen, and hydrogen, but he was unsuccessful.[60] The paper illustrates Brodie's faith in the possibility of finding mathematical solutions, or at least correlations, to the problems of chemistry.

In 1879 Brodie published a further defence of the Calculus[61] based on Victor Meyer's findings that at high temperatures the density of chlorine dropped to $\frac{2}{3}$ of its normal value. Meyer tentatively suggested that oxygen might have been given off from the chlorine when it was heated in a vertical tube (not horizontal!) and the chlorine collected over mercury. Oxygen was also formed when chlorine was treated with platinum and the resulting platinum chloride was decomposed. In each case about 1 % oxygen was formed.

Brodie seized on these results, coming from such a reputable authority, and showed how they could be explained by means of the Calculus. He produced a variety of equations which would cater for almost every conceivable reaction between oxygen, chlorine, hydrogen, and their compounds. In these he wrote the formula for chlorine as $\alpha\chi'^2\xi^2$. Two years later Victor Meyer retracted all his claims, and said that the oxygen must have been an impurity. However, by this time Brodie was dead, so he was saved any disappointment by this news. Even if Meyer's unlikely assertions had been true it would not have greatly helped the Calculus had chlorine contained oxygen. Brodie had drawn analogies between chlorine and the peroxides to prove that it was a compound element, but he had not suggested that it contained oxygen.[62] However, the lowering of the vapour pressure in Meyer's experiments could have been explained by the dissociation of chlorine into $\alpha\chi$ and χ, and it was probably this which primarily interested Brodie.

In the same year Naquet translated the Calculus into French, and Brodie had the Frenchman's criticisms translated and published in the *Philosophical Magazine*.[63] Firstly he said that the atomic theory was still useful because its predictions had led to the syntheses of phenols, the acids of the salicylic series, and the secondary and tertiary ammonias. The predictive value of atomism could be used without attaching any 'metaphysical' significance to the theory. He then asserted that had Brodie used the a^2 hypothesis the Calculus would be equivalent to the useful part of the atomic theory. At this point in the paper Brodie added a footnote saying that it was precisely because of the 'metaphysical signification' of atoms that he had decided to adopt the new system. Also the algebraical analysis of Part 2 of the Calculus could have no parallel in the atomic notation, and so the Calculus based on a^2 was not equivalent to the atomic theory.

Naquet then touched on the crucial point that isomers, which could be explained by the different grouping of atoms in the atomic theory, had no explanation in the Calculus. He repeated Kekulé's criticisms of choosing a as the base rather than a^2, and pointed out that the atomic system easily predicted the number of substitution products in substances like amines and hydrocarbons. Thus from the formula CH_4 it is obvious that there will be four substitution products CH_3Cl, CH_2Cl_2, $CHCl_3$, CCl_4. However, in the Calculus this substitution is written as an addition, thus

$$a^2\kappa + a\chi^2 = a\chi + a^2\kappa\chi$$

There seems to be no limit to the number of additions which could occur, and therefore no reason why CCl_5 should not be formed.[64]

Because of these criticisms, Naquet would oppose the introduction of the notation of the Calculus into chemistry; even if it were introduced, he would prefer the a^2 hypothesis because of the exceptions to the Law of Even Numbers of NO and NO_2. However, he did not therefore dismiss the Calculus as useless. He admitted that the introduction of algebra into chemistry was an important innovation, and he quoted the example of the wave and particle theories of light in physics as being an area in which two contradictory theories survived side by side;

the same might be true of the Calculus and the atomic theory. To this paper Naquet added a postscript about certain recent observations which pointed to the conclusion that hydrogen was evolved from some elements at very high temperatures.[65] He recognized that if this were true then it was a justification of the Calculus.

Brodie made a spirited reply to this paper[66] in which he showed that the number of substitution products could be predicted in the Calculus, although in rather a complicated way.

Taking the equation $H_2 + Cl_2 = 2HCl$

$$a + a\chi^2 = 2a\chi$$

therefore $a(\chi - 1)(\chi - 1) = 0$

This event occurs in two ways, by the substitution of 1 for χ.

The symbol for the unit of chlorine   is $a\chi\chi$
The symbol for the unit of hydrogen chloride is $a, 1, \chi$
The symbol for the unit of hydrogen   is $a, 1, 1$

He continues:

'Now the symbol 1 which appears in the symbols of hydrogen is not the symbol of any real weight, but is the symbol of an empty unit of space serving to mark the place where matter is not, but has been, and may be again. The explicit introduction of this symbol into the symbol of the unit of hydrogen limits the number of the operations χ (or any operation which may be substituted for χ) which may be performed upon a, the unit of hydrogen, to two.'[67]

Thus the symbol for methane is $a^2\kappa$ (1, 1, 1, 1) and only four successive substitutions are possible, shown in the following order.

$$a^2\kappa(1, 1, 1, 1) \quad CH_4$$
$$a^2\kappa(\chi, 1, 1, 1) \quad CH_3Cl$$
$$a^2\kappa(\chi, \chi, 1, 1) \quad CH_2Cl_2$$
$$a^2\kappa(\chi, \chi, \chi, 1) \quad CHCl_3$$
$$a^2\kappa(\chi, \chi, \chi, \chi) \quad CCl_4$$

There are no means of constructing $a^2\kappa\chi^2$.

In his conclusion Brodie asked Naquet to suspend judgment for a while on the question of isomers, adding a footnote that a large proportion of the elements which are compound in the Calculus had not been found in the sun because the sun's temperature was so high that they had been decomposed into hydrogen and the other prime factors.

In a second note, Naquet replied that Brodie had indeed successfully explained the process of substitution, but there remained two objections.

(a) If some elements are compound and some not it is strange that they should all obey Dulong and Petit's law.[68]

(b) The law of even numbers can be established for carbon compounds, but it cannot be so easily established for other series. It might be better to admit that the law was not universal than admit that chlorine and nitrogen are compound elements.

Naquet had translated Brodie's papers with the expressed intention of halting indifference to his work, 'since a new hypothesis opens new horizons to the investigator.' Such indifference was inexcusable now that Brodie had satisfactorily explained away one of Naquet's two principal objections to the Calculus, and he looked forward to learning of Brodie's solution to the problem of structural isomerism. However, it is worth recording that under the operational notation it would have been impossible for Brodie to explain it. Isomers are distinguished by differences in physical and chemical properties, and in preparation, but not in weight or composition. According to the Calculus there is only one symbol for each operation resulting in weight, and the chemical preparation is unimportant. However the operation is performed, its result is the same. As long as Brodie restricted himself to using only weight criteria to discriminate between substances it would not be possible for him to explain isomers. It is difficult to see how he could bring additional evidence to bear on this subject, as weight is the only criterion which can be used in chemical equations to determine operational formulae.

It is interesting to note that Crum Brown's earlier paper on 'The Application of Mathematics to Chemistry'[48] dealt with the subject of isomerism, and tried to express isomers mathematically. There has also been a recent attempt by a logician to explain isomers on a non-atomic basis.[69]

SECTION III. SOME FURTHER CRITICISMS OF THE CALCULUS

There are various chemical and mathematical points relevant to the Calculus which were not raised in published discussions. They will be discussed under various subject headings.

Mathematical Problems

The most pressing mathematical difficulty is that the distributive law, $x(y_1 + y_2) = xy_1 + xy_2$, is inconsistent with the fundamental equation of the Calculus, $x + y = xy$, as was pointed out by Jevons and Crum Brown.[70] This difficulty was also noticed by Donkin and De Morgan in private correspondence with Brodie.[71] In the second part of the Calculus Brodie amended this, and corrected the fundamental equation to

$$x + y = xy + 1$$

which is a particular example of the more general equation

$$mx + ny = x^m y^n + m + n - 1$$

This alteration makes the Calculus mathematically sound. However, Brodie could have achieved the same result by using the weight equation only.

$$w(xy) = w(x) + w(y)$$

where $w(xy)$ stands for the weight of the compound xy.

Using this equation,[72] chemical symbols can be built up in the following way:

Let oxygen $= a^n \xi^{n_1}$
Let water $= a^m \xi^{m_1}$

Then $2a^m \xi^{m_1} = a^n \xi^{n_1} + 2a$, from the fundamental equation, or

$$2mw(a) + 2m_1 w(\xi) = nw(a) + n_1 w(\xi) + 2w(a)$$

Then, provided that no two elements are integral multiples of a common factor, we can equate the coefficients thus,

$$2m = n + 2, \quad 2m_1 = n_1$$

This would give the same result as Brodie's correction. In some ways this alteration is similar to that suggested by Herschel privately.[73]

The importance of the weight criterion is again apparent in another anomaly touched on by Crum Brown which Brodie never admitted, namely the mathematical position of $2a\chi$. If the rules of the Calculus are observed, then the following transformation ought to be valid.

$$2a\chi = a\chi + a\chi = a^2\chi^2$$

This would have led to different factorization, and is obviously not lawful; but Brodie never explains why this transformation is not possible. The real criterion for what $2a\chi$ is, is determined by weight. The relative weights of the respective operations are

$$\chi = 17 \cdot 25 \quad a = 1$$

Thus $2a\chi = a\chi + a\chi = a(\chi + \chi) = a\chi^2$ is not allowed, as this has a relative weight of $35 \cdot 5$, making the weight equations unequal. Nor is $2a\chi = a\chi + a\chi = a^2\chi^2$ allowed, as this has a relative weight of $37 \cdot 5$, and there is no known compound which corresponds to this weight.

Factorization

It is somewhat surprising to note that if the atomic symbols are treated as algebraic terms, and if H_2O is treated as if it were H^2O (the square of the symbol H multiplied by the symbol O), then these symbols have properties almost identical with those of the Calculus. The following equations show this identity.

$$a^3\kappa^7\xi\chi + a^3\kappa^3\xi\mu = a\chi\mu + a^5\kappa^9\xi^2$$
$$a(a^2\kappa^7\xi - \mu)(\chi - a^2\kappa^2\xi) = 0 \qquad \ldots (a)$$

This equation in the atomic notation is

$$C_6H_5COCl + KOC_2H_5 = KCl + C_6H_5COOC_2H_5$$
$$(C_6H_5CO - K)(C_2H_5O - Cl) = 0 \qquad \ldots (b)$$

This equation is taken from the Calculus and, incidentally, shows how Brodie slipped in the symbol for potassium without the slightest justification, either from densities or from specific heats, for potassium is not one of the elements whose formula was determined in Part 1.

F

Provided that we are prepared to accept Brodie's criteria for interpretation, *i.e.*, that substitution or addition occurs whenever the equation is factorizable into brackets and without necessarily using his definition of 'cause,' then the atomic notation provides the same information as does the Calculus and factorization is not such a bizarre occurrence as might appear at first sight.

There are no alternative factors for the equation mentioned above, but in the case of polysubstitutions the atomic notation provides two possible factorizations, corresponding to the two ways in which the symbols may be interpreted, *e.g.*, $Cl_2 = Cl^2$ of $2Cl$.

In the following equation

$$Cl_2 + 2HI = I_2 + 2HCl$$

(*a*) If $x_2 = x^2$, $Cl^2 + 2HI - I^2 - 2HCl = 0$
$$(Cl - I)(Cl + I - 2H) = 0$$

therefore resolving, $(Cl - H)(Cl - I) = 0$ ... (1)
$$(I - H)(Cl - I) = 0$$ ... (2)

This is interpretable as the substitution of I for Cl twice on different compounds, Cl_2 and ICl, for when (1) and (2) are expanded they become,

$$Cl_2 + HI = HCl + ICl$$ ... (1)
$$ICl + HI = HCl + I_2$$ ... (2)

These are physically isolatable steps, and represent the two stages in the reaction mechanism.

(*b*) If $x_2 = 2x$, $2Cl + 2HI - 2I - 2HCl = 0$
$$(1 - H)(2Cl - 2I) = 0$$

This last equation is equally interpretable as iodine replacing chlorine in two steps, or the reverse of the addition of hydrogen. This happens wherever polysubstitution occurs. Only (*a*) is open to Brodie's symbols.

Most normalized equations can be factorized as above. In normalization a dummy factor is added in order to achieve factorization. It acts as a non-reacting compound to make the equation symmetrical and spatially accurate. It is not surprising that factorization should have emerged in an algebraic system such as the Calculus. Indeed it would be difficult to justify the Calculus at all if factorization and multiplication could not occur. There are, however, two interesting points, (a) why factorization should apply to the atomic notation, and (b) why factorization should take two physically interpretable forms.

The answer to the second point is mathematical. The Calculus was bound by strict mathematical rules in which x^2 and $2x$ had clearly defined, separate meanings. In the atomic notation either may be chosen to represent x_2, but they cannot both be used together. As long as they are separated, writing x^2 or $2x$ makes no difference to the factorization, one numerical symbolism having been changed for another. That is why $(x-a)^n$ in one factorization is equal to $n(x-a)$ in the other.

The answer to the first point is that as long as equations may be split into factors with two terms, and so become physically interpretable, algebraical factorization expresses mathematically that which the chemist chooses to represent by the rearrangement of chemical symbols. If the product of the brackets is equal to zero, as is always true in a chemical equation, then the equation vanishes when one of the symbols in the bracket is put equal to another in the same bracket; i.e., $(x-a)(y-b)=0$ vanishes when $a=x$.

This is similar to a chemical equation expressing substitution. This equation would vanish if the substitution on one side of the equation were reversed.

$$BaCl_2 + K_2SO_4 = BaSO_4 + 2KCl$$

If, on the left-hand side of the equation Cl_2 and SO_4 were interchanged, then the equation would again vanish, and this is expressed in the factorization, $(Ba - 2K)(2Cl - SO_4) = 0$.

Brodie's method has such a wide application because he breaks down the equations into their simplest steps and adds dummy factors (numbers) to make them symmetrical.

Dulong and Petit's Law

Dulong and Petit's law (hereafter referred to as DP) occupied a central position in the structure of the Calculus. In order to understand the reason for this it must be realized that the Calculus had a very limited range. Brodie gave the prime factors for only twenty elements in his papers, for reasons which we have already explained. The method of obtaining prime factors works for elements which can be vapourized. It works less well for elements which cannot, but it can give a reasonable value provided that all the other species in the dissociation are vapours, and that the element obeys DP. If two of the species cannot be vapourized, then much less information can be obtained, and if none of the products can be vapourized, then practically no information is available.

The reason why Brodie scarcely mentions any elements in Groups 1, 2 or 3 of the Periodic Table, or any of the transition metals, is that these elements and most of their compounds do not vapourize. The method of obtaining simple weights from vapour densities works satisfactorily for non-metals with covalent links, but in discussing metals Brodie has to use DP to get a value for 'the smallest weight of the elemental bodies formed by the decomposition of the unit of any chemical substance.' Accordingly he elevates it, along with Gay Lussac's Law of Gaseous Volumes, to its position as one of the pillars of the Calculus.

However, when we look more closely at the introduction of DP we find certain anomalies. Since Brodie uses DP to get a value for the simple weights of the metals, he cannot prove DP with reference to the metals, as this would assume his conclusion. Instead he has to turn to the non-metals. Brodie produces a table, purporting to prove DP, by giving the product of the specific heat and simple weight of the elements S, Se, I, Br, P, and As.[74] To a modern chemist it is surprising that any of these elements would obey DP, and it is fairly certain that Brodie used some extraordinary specific heats. However, the situation becomes even more bizarre when we realize that in the values given for the simple weights of these elements, *not one* corresponds to the atomic weight we would now use. In most cases it is the equivalent weight which is quoted, although, in the case of Br and I, it is half the equivalent weight. It seems to have been remarkably ingenious of Brodie to construct a table which even remotely corresponds to DP from these values. The constant value for the result must arise from the approximate equilibrium of two errors, a value for the specific heat which was too high, and a value for the atomic weight which was too low.

Even if we accept this remarkable table, it was still a sweeping assumption that because the law held for these six elements, none of them a true metal, it would also hold for all the other elements which would be discussed. The table did not even include all the elements whose simple weights and prime factors had already been determined, presumably because carbon, silicon and boron were well-known exceptions to DP.

There are two other interesting points about DP. The first is that in view of the different classes of elements which the Calculus proposed, and the corresponding difference in composition and formulae, it is a little surprising that a double element like θ^2 and a compound element like $\alpha\beta^2$ should both obey the law. Naquet was the first to notice this. Secondly, in the first group of elements which Brodie treats, all the simple weights are equivalent weights, and the formulae are derived from the consideration of hydrogen as one unit. When it comes to elements treated by means of DP, this method should give their true atomic weights. However, if this were so, then the compounds which involved an element from the first group, and one from the third group, the weight equations would get mixed up, as half the compound would be in equivalents and half in atomic weights. Brodie leaves an escape clause which prevents this when he asserts that $A = V$, or $\dfrac{V}{2}$, or $\dfrac{V}{4}$. Thus the atomic weight can be divided by 2 or 4 to make it agree with the equivalent weight.

Some Empirical Criticisms

Brodie suggests that there are three categories of elements:

(1) Simple elements α, δ
(2) Double elements ξ^2, θ^2
(3) Compound elements $\alpha\chi^2$

There is no empirical justification for this division, other than that the second group has an even valency, a point which Brodie did not realize, although Odling did give a justification along those lines. Furthermore, there is no resemblance between the properties of the elements in the same group, or any correlation with Mendeleev's Periodic Law. It is also difficult to explain why the elements have such similar formulae. If it were mere chance that the prime factors had cooled down in these combinations from the high temperatures involved in the formation of the earth, there seems to be no reason why they should have such similar formulae.

A number of chemical objections arise in connection with Brodie's remarks about factorization, and the results of the definition of 'cause'. In the first place, because of the existence of the compound elements like $\alpha\chi^2$, it was often possible to factorize out α in chemical equations. This gave a rather misleading 'cause' of the reaction, and in extreme cases it obscured the difference between addition and substitution.

The definition of 'cause' places two unnecessary restrictions on explanations. The first is that Brodie implies, apparently unintentionally, that equations which do not factorize can never be explained. He opens Section IV of Part 2 thus:

'The explanation of a chemical event consists in referring the event to the causes which concur to produce it. Therefore it is only those events which can be thus expressed which can, in any proper sense, be said to be explained.'

Thus an explanation of these equations is not only empirically impossible, but also logically impossible. As there are a number of such reactions, *e.g.*, polymerizations, this seems too restrictive. Secondly, non-stoichiometric equations are not catered for in the Calculus, as they cannot be expressed by means of an equation. This again is rather restrictive since much useful information can be obtained from approximate results.

SECTION IV. BRODIE AS A PHILOSOPHER

The conception and development of the Calculus are closely linked with Brodie's views on the aims of science and its limitations in the description and explanation of observable phenomena. While it is probably not true to say that Brodie first adopted a philosophical position and then invented the Calculus to justify it, he was certainly not led directly to the Calculus from his chemical researches, and he was greatly influenced by a number of philosophers. His philosophical standpoint so interacted with his experimental work and guided the direction of his research and its interpretation that analysis of his views is important.

Brodie considered atoms to be an unnecessary interpolation between observation and expression; unnecessary and also confusing, as they are not subject to any particular rules, but can be manipulated at will, and they invite us to think of chemical phenomena in terms of the movements of real balls. However, the true object of science is not to explain, but to describe. We cannot ask what water is,[75] only what it does, or what it becomes. We have no means of grasping the underlying 'reality' of things, and so should content ourselves with the accurate description of what things do. To do this, we must sweep away every unnecessary and confusing image and return to the facts of chemistry. We must represent these by means of suitable symbols which have known rules by which we may manipulate them, each symbol corresponding to an observable fact. In this way we can provide a true record of chemical events and ignore those 'ideas that the science of chemistry has no other field for its activity than the obscure region of atomic speculations.'[76] Thus the Calculus in conception (if not in execution, as we shall see later) is in the positivist tradition. Metaphysics is shunned; every proposition must be verified by observation; propositions which contain the term 'atom' cannot be verified, so the term must not be used. Thus a new theory of chemistry is built up, based on the solid, enduring facts of Gay Lussac's Law and that of Dulong and Petit.

Many of the points raised by Brodie are answered by a closer enquiry into the nature of theories and laws; how they arise; and what are their objectives and limitations. Ignoring the question of what exactly constitutes a law-like statement, as this is not strictly relevant to the present discussion, there are three obvious ways in which theories differ from laws.[77]

(1) Historically, theories follow experimental laws, because laws are logically less general, and also because laws are empirically testable, whereas theories are not. Thus the law of constant composition is experimentally testable, but the atomic theory is

not, as it is an explanation of the facts of chemistry, and there are other explanations which are as logically valid; *i.e.*, that all substances have spirits in them which act by their own volition. There is no experimental way of finding which theory is false, although the atomic theory may be more useful.

(2) Often the sole ground for believing in a theory at an early stage is that it correlates observables and laws which were previously considered unrelated. This is certainly true of the atomic theory, which at first only correlated the law of constant composition and the laws of multiple and reciprocal proportions. This claim could not be made for the Calculus. Allied to this there is the fact that laws still hold when theories change. The law may be incorporated into the theory, and the language of the theory may be used in the law, but the law is still unintelligible without the theory, because the law is empirically testable, and only deals with observable phenomena. The meanings of the terms in a law are fixed by the phenomena with which they are correlated. However, when theories change, the actual theoretical terms change with them. Theoretical notions cannot be understood apart from the theory, as this implicitly defines them. When the fundamental postulates of a theory are altered, the meanings of the basic terms alter, even if the same linguistic terms are used.

(3) In general, laws are one statement, whereas theories comprise several related statements. Where laws explain or describe the correlation between two observables, theories explain a large number of laws and observations. A good example of this is the difference between Boyle's law and the kinetic theory. Theories also predict new experimental laws.

Having differentiated between theories and laws, let us now examine the structure of a theory. There are three major components in most theories.

(*a*) The abstract calculus which is the logical skeleton of the explanatory system, and which defines the basic notions.

(*b*) The set of rules that assign empirical content to the calculus by tying certain parts of it to observables. These are widely known as correspondence rules.

(*c*) The model of the calculus which puts it into familiar or visual terms. The object of a theory is to explain the unknown in terms of the known, and in this connection the model plays a crucial role.

In the present discussion it is vital to distinguish between the correspondence rules and the model. In understanding a theory it is important to understand the correspondence rules, and the following five points apply to the use of these rules.

(1) Correspondence rules are the only rules which connect the theory to observables.

(2) They do not tie bits of the models to observables.

(3) They do not furnish explicit definitions; *i.e.*, they do not provide the means whereby one word or phrase in a theory can be replaced by an observable. They only provide rules whereby theoretical concepts may be indirectly checked.

(4) Correspondence rules are often not stated explicitly or precisely, but are occasionally the necessary and/or sufficient conditions for describing an experimental condition in theoretical language.

(5) Not all the terms in a theory need have correspondence rules. It is the mark of a developing theory that as the experimental results accumulate, latent correspondence rules are formulated which are adapted to the new conditions.

In these terms Brodie's Calculus and his criticisms of the atomic theory are seen in a new light. First of all, Brodie's criticism that the atomic notation did not have rules by which the signs could be manipulated was irrelevant since it had a consistent set of correspondence rules which alone were necessary. These were used to explain the laws of constant composition, multiple proportions and reciprocal proportions. The atomic theory did not have correspondence rules for all its concepts, and in particular it did not provide an adequate explanation for valency; but as we have seen it is not necessary to have rules for all theoretical concepts. There are some concepts in a theory which serve no other function initially than to bind the theory together and make it consistent. This is exemplified in the model. All the theoretical constructs must be identifiable in the model, but not necessarily tied to correspondence rules. One of the chief advantages of the atomic theory was that it was adaptable to the new constructs of valency and isomerism; thus new correspondence rules were discovered which substantiated the theory. On the other hand the Calculus did not have the necessary correspondence rules; Brodie sacrificed these for internal consistency. There were rules for the manipulation of the symbols, but no definite rules, explicit or implicit, for tying these to observation. This is shown in the difficulty mentioned about the interpretation of $2a\chi$.

Neither was the Calculus sufficiently adaptable to meet the needs of new discoveries, as is readily apparent. On the above analysis the difference between the Calculus and the atomic theory was that the Calculus had no model. However, in many cases the separation of the abstract calculus from the model is either not possible, or it destroys the value of a theory. Models have the following invaluable assets.

(*a*) They are invariably based on systems of known properties; *i.e.*, they explain the unknown in terms of the known. Because of this they are of great value in the formulation of correspondence rules as they provide a guide to distinguish which parts of a calculus are likely to be relevant and which are not. On the atomic model it was easy to show the analogies which were likely to hold, and which were not. But in the Calculus it was not possible to explain why chemical reactions occurred, or why only parts of the Calculus were used, or why chemical elements had only three types of formulae.

(*b*) Because models operate under laws which are familiar, they suggest ways of expanding the theory, and are of great predictive value. The most fruitful linguistic expression used in science is the analogy. It is by means of the analogies suggested by a model that a theory may be expanded and tested. This heuristic content of a model is perhaps its most important asset.

Thus, a theory must almost invariably contain a model. Brodie's Calculus does not, and is more a compendium of events than a means of explanation and discovery. This is a common failing in positivist thought. For if every event is to have its own symbol, then the predictive value of the concept is zero. It is not the *fault* of theories that they have models which do not correspond exactly to events, this is their great *advantage*, for the analogies suggested by the models provide the opportunity for further research which will either expand the theory or make it collapse and require its replacement.

Brodie's Definition of 'Cause'

One of Brodie's main contentions was that science cannot explain nature to us; it merely describes. We can never know the 'real' nature of things. On one level this is merely a semantic problem. For if science only describes, and does not explain, what constitutes an explanation? If theories only describe facts, then what do we use to explain them? If we never explain anything, but only describe it, we misuse language, since we could dispense with the word 'explain.' Thus to say that theories describe, but do not explain, is futile, as we have no criteria for the use of the word 'explain'.

Brodie, however, was concerned with a much deeper problem. One of the most general uses of the word 'explanation' implies the process of cause and effect; we say we have explained something if we have shown its cause. What kind of necessity is involved in cause? Descriptivists argue that, since the sciences do not involve logical, but merely contingent, relations, they do not answer the question 'why', but only the question 'how.' This assumes that the only answer to the question 'why' is one which involves the inherent necessity of the proposition. However, in common usage, this is not the case, for it is quite legitimate to say that science answers the question 'why' *and* 'explains,' according to the well-established usage of these terms.

However, there is a further problem here. The descriptivist objects to the assumption that the laws of nature are more than contingently true. This hinges on the Humean analysis of cause; *i.e.*, when we say that event *A* causes event *B*, all we mean is that whenever we observe *A*, we then observe *B*, so we have come to expect that *B* follows *A* without fail. However, cause and effect implies more than contingency, although it does not involve logical necessity. So how do we use 'cause' and why do we use it when we do?

At present the Principle of Causality is regarded as a methodological rule throughout the sciences. To give an example: in Newtonian mechanics the earth and the solar system did not obey the Newtonian rules within the limits of experimental error. This did not lead physicists to abandon Newtonian mechanics; they postulated a new planet, Neptune, to which the discrepancy would be due. They predicted where Neptune would be at a certain time and, looking there, they found it. In this case the Principle of Causality was useful as a research guide, and it may be judged by its success.

However, when we turn to Brodie, we find that his definition of 'cause' was in no way predictive.[78] He obviously realized that there was a discrepancy between his descriptive analysis of phenomena and causal analysis since he tried to remedy it by redefining cause. But Brodie's definition of 'cause' in no way constitutes an explanation in the normal sense in which we use the word. Substitution is not explained because factorization is possible. Since factorization, as we have seen, is a juxtaposition of empirical classification, and 'cause' is described in terms of factorization, the 'cause' is really a *redescription* of events. To be consistent, Brodie should have redescribed the observed facts in his own terms (factorization), and admitted that he was using, not causal, but descriptive, terminology. Then he could still have described chemistry in terms of the transference of 'bits of matter,' as he did at the end of Part 2.

Even then the Calculus, although consistent, would still have been deficient in predictive power, because we have seen that the Principle of Causality is a tool for the discovery of hidden parameters, and any theory which does not use this tool lacks some of the apparatus to enlarge and predict.

Brodie, Boole, and Condillac[79]

The most cursory glance at the Calculus reveals how much Brodie owed to George Boole's *Mathematical Analysis of Logic*, and Brodie himself recognized this. The parallels between his method and that of Brodie's are striking, as a short account of Boole's method will show. Boole used algebraic symbols as operations. The operation which each symbol performed was that of selection of a class of objects from a larger class. The numerical symbol 1 was used as the symbol of the universe, and the totality of objects in the universe. Thus we have $x = x1$. Using these elective symbols Boole defined xy as the successive operation of x and y on the universe. From these premises he discovered three fundamental laws which governed the use of the symbols. They were, (1) the distributive law, (2) the commutative law, (3) the index law that $x^n = x$. This applied because the operation of selecting the class of objects with properties X from any other class yields the same result no matter how many times it is done in succession.

It is worth noting that the use of these rules does not lead to any mathematical contradiction, unlike those of Brodie's Calculus. By means of these rules Boole expressed logical forms like the syllogism, hypothetical, etc., in a mathematical form, and discovered certain logical relations which had previously been overlooked. The method had the advantage that the properties of these forms were made obvious at a glance, and the use of logical forms was no longer a tortuous and time-consuming labour.

In view of the similarity of technique, what went wrong with Brodie's Calculus in comparison with that of Boole? One of the reasons for Brodie's failure was the use of the term 'operation' which we shall discuss later. Another was the fact that Brodie produced an inconsistent algebra. However, these were minor reasons compared with the following fundamental shortcomings. These may be illustrated by a comparison of passages from Boole's *Logic* and Brodie's Calculus. From Boole:

> 'Let it be granted that the problem which had baffled the efforts of ages is not a hopeless one; that the "science of real existence" and "the research of causes" . . . do not transcend the limits of the human intellect. I am then compelled to assert, that according to this view of the nature of Philosophy, *Logic forms no part of it.* On the principle of a true classification, we ought no longer to associate Logic and Metaphysics, but Logic and Mathematics.'[80]

From Brodie:

> 'A symbol, however, should be something more than a convenient and compendious expression of facts. It is, in the strictest sense, an instrument for the discovery of facts, and is of value mainly with reference to this end, by its adaptation to which it is to be judged.' [81]

Boole realized that his was an analytical system, and that he had to divorce it from the realm of speculation. His mathematical techniques produced results because they used a rigorous shorthand to deal successfully with the intricate problems of logic. While logic became internally consistent, it ceased to be of practical value to the philosopher. Brodie, on the other hand, was trying to get the best of both worlds, by building up an analytic system *and* making it applicable to the real world. He failed by his own criterion, that a system should be 'an instrument for the discovery of facts.'

Brodie acknowledged his debt to Condillac in Part 1 of the Calculus where he wrote that his aim had been:

> 'no other than to free the science of chemistry from the trammels imposed upon it by accumulated hypotheses, and to endow it with the most necessary of all the instruments of progressive thought, an exact and rational language. "Tout langue est un méthode analytique, et toute méthode analytique est une langue"—Condillac.'[82]

Condillac had been mainly interested in the uses and abuses of language. He took analytical mathematics to be the exemplar of language and he regarded algebra as a set of exact symbols to be manipulated by conventions. By agreement they always mean the same, and there is no admixture of our own judgment in them. By using language we rationalize, classify, and communicate experience. More than that, 'we think only through the medium of words.' Thus we must make every effort to clarify and sharpen our thought; we must make certain that every word in our language corresponds to an object or determinate idea, and that it is not a metaphysical figment. In a complex situation, to name is to discover, for to name any part of the situation is to analyse it into smaller components. In this sense analysis and naming become a single act, and: 'The art of reasoning is nothing more than a language well arranged.' In science we can find a rational language by which we can classify things, and which we can use systematically.

It is easy to see how Brodie was attracted to this philosophy but his eagerness to apply it to chemistry led him to make some unjustifiable claims on behalf of the Calculus. Thus, in asserting that the Calculus was a discovery because it could not be deduced from an existing notation, he misunderstood Condillac by confusing taxonomy with discovery. A new nomenclature and non-deducibility from existing systems are only two of the criteria for discovery. A more important criterion is that the new system should predict results which are experimentally verified. It was here that the Calculus failed.[83]

A favourite theme of Brodie's, repeated in *Ideal Chemistry* and in the discussion of Williamson's lecture, is exemplified in the following passage from Part I. 'We cannot adopt the atomic symbol and at the same time declare ourselves free from the atomic doctrines.'[84] The connection with Condillac is obvious, but it is almost as obvious where Brodie has overstepped the mark. Chemists could legitimately use the atomic theory as the most useful of the time, without necessarily committing themselves to a belief in the physical existence of atoms. The atomic theory certainly correlated a large number of facts, but there was no direct evidence for atoms, and most scientists kept an open mind on the subject. In any case, as Williamson pointed out, it was impossible to know what atoms were; whether they were round balls, or balls with hooks, or geometrical shapes which fitted together, or centres of force.

Even ignoring these points, Brodie's adherence to the principles of Condillac was rather unfortunate. Condillac had been writing at the end of the eighteenth century when taxonomy was the most important task of science. At that time attention was shifting from the abstract to the experimental and descriptive sciences, from astronomy and theoretical physics to experimental physics, natural history, and chemistry. These sciences presented a mass of uncoordinated facts which needed classification and pigeonholing, a task largely completed by Linnaeus and Lavoisier. By the 1860s the task was of a different kind. Although advances in preparative and organic chemistry were not paralleled by concomitant advances in theory the need was not for a retreat to the basic facts, but for the imagination to evolve theories which would embrace the newly discovered information. The ingenious conception of the Calculus shows Brodie's imagination to be the equal of such innovators as Kekulé, van't Hoff, and le Bel, but, compared with them, he was moving in the wrong direction by adopting a positivist standpoint. There was certainly room for scepticism about the atomic theory, but although most chemists recognized its shortcomings, very few tried to remedy them. In his remedy Brodie took one path and Kekulé and van't Hoff took the other. Unfortunately Brodie's was a blind alley.

Operations

'From the former point of view [*i.e.*, the Calculus] we consider the operations, from the latter [the atomic theory] the result of operations.'[85]

Brodie anticipated by some sixty years the man who gets most of the credit for postulating operationalism, P. W. Bridgman. In *The Logic of Modern Physics* Bridgman proposed that the definition of any term must include an operation: 'The concept is synonymous with the corresponding set of operations.'[86] For example, the term 'harder than' might be operationally defined by the rule that a piece of mineral X is to be called harder than another piece of mineral Y if the operation of drawing a sharp point of X across the surface of Y results in a mark on the latter. Similarly, the different numerical values of quantity, such as length, are thought of as operationally definable by reference to the outcome of specified measuring operations. By using this definition Bridgman thought that he could exclude non-observational and redundant terms from the scientific vocabulary.

In order to make this technique applicable to all of our concepts, Bridgman had to introduce two kinds of operations.[87]

(1) Instrumental operations in which various devices of observation and measurement are used.

(2) Symbolic operations, or verbal and mental operations.

The following basic principles of operational analysis are relevant. (*a*) To understand the meaning of a term, we must know the operational criteria for its application. Every meaningful scientific term must therefore permit of an operational definition. (*b*) To avoid ambiguity, every scientific term should be defined by means of one unique operational definition. Even when two different operational procedures (*e.g.*, the optical and tactual ways of measuring length) have been found to yield the same results, they should be considered as defining different concepts which should be distinguished terminologically. (*c*)

Hypotheses incapable of operational testing, or questions involving untestable formulations, are meaningless by the operational criterion.

In relating Brodie's Calculus to these criteria, we must admit that his operations were not as straightforward as he would have us believe. Although 'making hydrogen' may be a, Brodie admitted that to make oxygen required two such operations, ξ and ξ. What kind of operations are these? They are certainly not physical, because it only requires one of these to make oxygen however it is made. Brodie tried to clarify this point by using the analogy of hydrogen being similar to one musical note, while oxygen is similar to two notes of different pitch.[88] Elsewhere he compared the operations to hammer blows on a piece of iron, since they shape the compounds from simple weights.[89] However, these diverse analogies do not help clarify the nature of the operations. If they were physical operations, Brodie would not have arrived at compound elements, as the elements cannot be made by any operations, and therefore should have been the starting points for the building up of compounds by means of physical operations.

Brodie's ambiguous use of the term 'operation' was a result of his method of constructing symbols for the elements. Starting from the postulate that hydrogen was indivisible, he built up the symbols for the other elements from the *equations* into which they entered. This is the reverse of the technique introduced by Lavoisier, in which substances which cannot be decomposed are defined as elements and given simple symbols. The symbol of a compound is then constructed by analysing the compound into its elements and we build up our equations by means of these symbols. Brodie, on the other hand, classified the equations first, and then derived his formulae. This is illustrated in an early paper[90] in which he classified equations according to the *volumes* of reactants and products involved, and not according to the chemical similarities between different reactants and products.

Brodie thought that it was 'obvious, from the way in which the symbol is constructed, that the properties symbolized are the properties of that system of chemical equations into which the symbols enter, and from which the laws of the science are to be deduced.'[91] However, the reasoning which led him to adopt this singular point of view requires some explanation. He believed that since we can never know what matter really is, but only what it does, we gain most profit from studying the changes in matter. These changes are described in chemical equations. Since we cannot classify matter, we classify observable changes in matter. Thus we classify equations, which are the record of these changes. To do this we must make the equations mathematically consistent and accurate by means of the Calculus. Thus classification in terms of equations can be reduced to the belief that we can never know anything about matter, a contention which we have already shown to be without foundation.[92]

Is it nevertheless possible to make the Calculus operationally sound? This might be achieved if we defined the operations as physical ones, and then only used one symbol for each element. Such alterations would, however, involve grave difficulties of the kind which apply also to Bridgman's operations. For, as we have seen, it is very difficult to fit isomers and allotropes into this system. In the first place, each allotrope would require a different symbol; on the other hand, optical isomers, which can be obtained by the same series of operations, violate the rule that a product is uniquely determined by its operation.

Bridgman's operations are suspect for two reasons. Firstly, the symbolic operation is a very loosely defined term: to distinguish between lawful and unlawful mental acts is a somewhat unrewarding task. Secondly, we should not, strictly speaking, use a word such as length when speaking of measurements as different as the width of a pin and the distance to Mars. As each is measured by a different operation, each should have a different nomenclature. However, this problem can only be avoided by admitting that, in our conceptual framework, words such as mass and length are useful because they can be cross-checked within a theoretical framework, such as Newtonian mechanics. Similarly, theories may contain non-observational terms which serve only to make the theory self-consistent, and which can only be defined by other terms in the theory.

Brodie and Bridgman were both working at a time of crisis in their respective fields. Both tried to resolve the crisis by using operations. It is true that the more rigorous analysis provided by Bridgman has been helpful in weeding out unnecessary terms in physics, but it needs to be greatly modified to deal with theoretical terms. Operationism seems to be a positivist retreat at a time of crisis in a science. Positivists tend to think that the only solutions is to go right back to the facts, and to discard as many theoretical terms as possible. In some circumstances this policy may be justified, but it is certainly not the only solution, and in other cases more imagination, faith, or merely a wider use of current theoretical concepts is necessary.

Mathematics

Lastly, and briefly, we consider the reasons why Brodie insisted on a strict mathematical analysis of an operational model, and why he used algebra as his tool. The latter must be attributed partly to the influence of Condillac, and partly to the success of Boole's application of algebra to logic. However, although algebra is probably the most adaptable mathematical form, the laws of multiple and reciprocal proportions render chemistry more susceptible to an arithmetical treatment.

Clearly Brodie believed that a mathematical calculus afforded a method of describing the facts of chemistry which was more rigorous and certain than any talk of atoms floating in space. Mathematical truths are certainties, and he felt that if the facts of chemistry could be embodied in mathematics, they too would be certainties. Mathematics is the ideal abstraction at which we would arrive if all experimental error could be abolished. No one has refuted this more succinctly than Bridgman, who wrote:

'This is no academic matter, but touches the essence of the situation. There is no longer any basis for the idealization of mathematics, and for the view that our imperfect knowledge of nature is responsible for failure to find the precise relations of mathematics. It is the mathematics made by us which is imperfect and not our knowledge of nature. . . . The concepts of mathematics are inventions made by us in an attempt to describe nature. . . . The problem is to make our equations correspond more closely to the physical experience back of them.'[93]

Thus 'rigour' and mathematical consistency are not the only objectives of a scientific theory.[94] All laws are approximate, but it is these approximations which are at the boundaries of science, and which are the stepping stones to further progress.

III

Some Correspondence connected with Sir Benjamin Brodie's Calculus of Chemical Operations

by

W. H. Brock

From the range of possible attitudes towards atomism which were articulated publicly and privately during the nineteenth century, it will probably be agreed that the most interesting was the positivism of Sir Benjamin Collins Brodie, the Aldrichian, and later Waynflete Professor of Chemistry at Oxford from 1855 until 1872; for he was one of the few sceptical chemists who seriously attempted to develop a rival system to atomism.

Brodie was born in London in 1817, the son of the famous surgeon and President of the Royal Society of the same name from whom he inherited a baronetcy in 1862. At the age of eleven he went to Harrow school from where he won a Classics scholarship to Caius College, Cambridge. However, his father preferred him to be educated as a Commoner, so in 1835 Brodie joined a brilliant circle of future eminent Victorians—Jowett, Stanley, Lake, Clough and Hobhouse[1]—at Balliol College, Oxford, where his interests turned away from Classics to Mathematics. He took a second-class honours in the latter subject in 1838, but because of his agnosticism and refusal to assent to the Thirty-Nine Articles, he was unable until 1860 to obtain the M.A. degree essential for a respectable academic career at Oxford.[2] For some time after graduation Brodie trained for the Bar at Lincoln's Inn in the chambers of his uncle, Peter Brodie, who specialized in conveyancy; but finding that he disliked the law, he decided to study chemistry with Liebig at Giessen. Since he seems to have moved in Royal Institution circles at this period, it is not improbable that Brodie was attracted to science by the example of Faraday, although, of course, the influence of his father who was a friend of Liebig's[3] cannot be overlooked.

At Giessen Brodie began a friendship with his future opponent, Alexander Williamson, and did some original and highly praised analyses of the different waxes which Grundlach had produced by feeding bees on different sugars.[4] This work, for which he gained a Royal Medal of the Royal Society in 1850, as well as a Fellowship of the Society in 1849 independently of his father's influence, proved the existence of solid alcohols that were homologous with the known alcohols, and it had important implications for the understanding of animal metabolism.

On his return to England Brodie married and set up a private laboratory in London where he taught chemistry to his intimate friend and later colleague at Oxford, Nevil Story Maskelyne.[5] Here he also began the experimental work on peroxides with which his name is always connected. In a paper[6] published in 1850 on the condition of elements at the moment of chemical change Brodie tried to reconcile Berzelian electrochemical dualism with the newer ideas concerning the multiatomicity of some elements. In order to explain why like atoms *could* cohere and need not repel as Berzelius's polarity theory implied, Brodie suggested that opposite electrical charges were induced at moments of chemical change and that chemical change always involved decomposition or dissociation. The kind of charge depended on the nature of the compound of which the element was a component before the change took place. He thought that the behaviour of peroxides was a crucial test for his theory. In the reduction of silver oxide by hydrogen peroxide Brodie's theory suggested that the second oxygen atom in peroxide was in an unstable condition so that when it was brought into contact with silver oxide a true 'synthesis' of diatomic oxygen occurred.

$$\overset{+\ -\ +\ \ -\ +\ \ -}{H\ O\ O\ \ OAg_{\frac{1}{2}}Ag_{\frac{1}{2}}} = HO + O_2 + Ag \qquad [O = 8]$$

This is a key paper in Brodie's development as a chemist for it reveals his open mind concerning the question of the decomposition of the chemical 'elements,' and it explains both his intense interest in allotropy which he thought was due to the arrangement and charge of the particles making up an element, and his preoccupation with peroxides because they offered ideal experimental material for the development of his positivist ideas concerning the classification of chemical reactions.

By 1850 therefore, Brodie had established himself as an important chemist. From 1850 to 1854 he was Secretary of the Chemical Society, and in 1860 he became its President. During the decade 1850-60 he published fundamental experimental studies of the allotropic modifications of sulphur, phosphorus and carbon.[7] He found that iodine catalyzed the conversion of yellow into red phosphorus through unstable intermediates; and that pure graphite, when treated with potassium chlorate, formed a crystalline acid which he named 'graphitic acid,' $C_{11}H_4O_5$. Since the analogous acid of silicon contained the molecule Si_4, Brodie suggested that graphitic acid might contain a graphite radical, $(Gr)_4$. In that case graphite might be a distinct element, of weight 33, which was capable of forming its own salts; modern studies have confirmed the existence of such salts.

The other principal theme of Brodie's work during the 1850s was his research on the preparation and reactions of peroxides which culminated in 1863 with the discovery of the explosive organic peroxides.[8]

In 1855, despite some opposition from the theological Fellows, Brodie was elected to the Aldrichian Chair of Chemistry at Oxford where he did much to gain recognition for chemistry as an academic subject as well as proper laboratory facilities for its study.[9] Ten years later, in 1865, Brodie's Chair was renamed the Waynflete, but because of his marriage no College Fellowship was ever offered to him. He resigned from the Chair in 1872 because of ill-health, and retired soon afterwards to a magnificent house on the top of Box Hill in Surrey. However, he did not immediately stop his experimental work, for in the same year he published a paper on the action of electricity on oxygen and carbon dioxide which confirmed Odling's suggestion, and Soret's proof, that the ozone molecule was triatomic,[10] and introduced the well-known elementary apparatus for the preparation of ozone, 'Brodie's ozonizer.' Although Brodie related this work to the notation of the Calculus, his other researches during retirement seem to have been purely a continuation of this electrical work and irrelevant to his views on chemical reactions. These researches included the synthesis of organic compounds by sparking carbon monoxide with hydrogen, published in 1873.[11]

Brodie died in November 1880 from rheumatic fever, with the Calculus on which he had spent twenty years of his life uncompleted.[12] He 'was a man of great originality and wide range of interests. He was an indefatigable worker at chemical problems, and his love of literature, and of poetry in particular, was as great as his love of science.'[13] His published works clearly show him to have been a patient and painstaking investigator. His chemical technique and analyses were excellent, as exemplified in the papers on graphite and the later one on ozone, where he made considerable technical improvements on the work of his contemporaries including the method of estimating gas volumes by measuring the pressure required to bring a mercury surface exactly to a glass point in a cylinder. His preparative skill was also very great, as shown by his description of the preparation of barium peroxide and the organic peroxides. His imagination is obvious right from the paper of 1850, and if the logic of his deductions may occasionally be questioned, his ability to correlate isolated facts into a conceptual scheme may not be doubted.

During the summer of 1964, the University of Leicester received from Brodie's granddaughters[14] the gift of a box containing a preserved sample of Brodie's scientific correspondence. The majority of these letters are for the year 1867, and are concerned with the Calculus. Many prominent names are featured, and since these letters throw a considerable light on both the Calculus and its reception, and therefore on contemporary attitudes towards atomism, they are here published in full. To complete the collection letters have been added from the archives of the Royal Society, from the University of London's De Morgan Collection, and from the Museum of History of Science at Oxford. In the transcriptions I have not rendered deletions except when they are obviously more than slips of the pen; they are then set in square brackets and the

interpolated material set off by //. The handwriting of Williamson and Brodie is particularly excruciating, and in their letters,
and in a few others, where it has not been possible to complete
a transcription, or to guess a meaning, the missing words are
symbolized by asterisks. The order of the letters is roughly
chronological and to afford continuity to them, an explanatory
commentary has been placed before each item.

*

In the first letter, written immediately after Brodie's paper
had been read to the Royal Society in 1866, Williamson revealed
his doubts about the need for Brodie's Ideal Chemistry.

1. FROM A. W. WILLIAMSON   LONDON 1866[15]

Univ. Coll.
Friday 4 May [1866]

My dear Brodie,

I should have been glad to see something more of you while
in town to talk over your paper. Are you likely to be up again
soon? My unceasing engagement prevents me from getting out
of town as often as I would wish to as I visit my Father at
Brighton so that I fear our only chance of meeting for some
time hence will be here. I have taken the liberty of marking in
pencil on your paper some small verbal matters which struck
me on reading it. They are at pages: 24, 29, 36, 37.[16]

Your definition of a chemical operation as an operation of
which the result is a *weight* involves a use of the word weight so
very different from the accepted use that it does shock a good
deal. I stated at the Society yesterday that I have not sufficiently
familiarized myself with the substance of your paper to be able
to do justice to its details and every opinion which I now form
respecting the details may themselves be altered by better
information but it does seem to me at present that the assumptions which you make in establishing the symbols of the elements
are coextensive with those of the atomic theory.[17] You perform
in obedience to the laws of your symbolic notation various
analytical transformations which are the equivalent of our
customary reasonings and which cannot fail to shew fruits such

as reasoning with symbols does in every department to which it is applied.

It is certainly impossible to overrate the importance of this step and there is doubtless far less risk of error in the simple reckonings with symbols than in ordinary thinking.

Are you quite sure that it is expedient to abandon the words element atom molecule, &c. and to substitute your terms for them? Also to disuse[18] *"weight"* in its natural abstract sense and use it: weight of some particular substance which I take to be your meaning. Of course you have thought over the matter fully and have definite answers for the course adopted. You will have some idea from the above lines, of the impression made on me at first.

Yours sincerely

Alex. W. Williamson

William Odling, who was suspicious of atoms, had favourably anticipated the publication of Brodie's new notation in 1864.[19] Later, as a member of the Royal Society's Council, he had re-fereed Brodie's paper with the help of the physicist George Stokes.[20] In the following letter Odling, in his other capacity of Secretary to the Chemical Society, asked Brodie to give a popular exposition of his Calculus to the Chemical Society—a 'memorable and interesting evening in the life of the Society which took place in June 1867.[21] Odling's letter clearly indicates the perplexity of contemporary chemists, and even physicists, when faced by Brodie's abstract system.

2. FROM W. ODLING   LONDON 1866[22]

St. Bartholomew's E.C.

November 6th [1866]

My dear Sir Benjamin,

I suppose Harcourt[23] told you that your paper was ordered for publication at the R.S. Council meeting on Thursday last and that he and I had been deputed by the Chem. Soc. Council to ask you to give us a popular account of your calculus some evening before Xmas say on December 6th or 20th. I hope you will not mind my telling you what was said of the character of your paper especially as I was I may say deputed to let you know it. It was thought that you had probably arrived at your very abstract notions by starting in the first instance from ** ones, so that it was scarcely possible for those who had not gone through a similar process to follow your explanation begun and elaborated from the abstract point of view. Even Stokes[24] to whom I suppose abstractions of any degree are pretty familiar complained that until he came to the demonstrations he could not understand the gist of your scheme and even after reverting to your first part did not feel sure that he had appreciated its weight. For myself I believe that after considerable pains I do understand it, and though staggered by some of the results, and inclined to dispute some of the propositions with you, entertain a very high opinion of the value of your method and of the importance of making it generally known and understood. Now if in addressing our society you will look upon your auditors as children requiring to be gradually led up to the fundamental notion, rather than as philosophers competent to take it in at a glance and make deductions from it you will I think stand a better chance in awakening a general interest and real consideration of your conceptions. I hope you will not take these remarks amiss especially as I can hardly acknowledge an individual responsibility for them—though from a common feeling with you on many points I have an individual interest in the dissemination and right comprehension of the views which you have propounded. Will you please let me // or Harcourt // have an answer before the next Council meeting on the 15th instant.

I suppose that like most of us here you have been amused by Frankland's marvellous picture book.[25] There is a paragraph in the middle of page 151 of Laurent's method (English Edition) which I think very applicable to a good deal of F.[26] You will I am sure regret to learn that there has been [** . . . **] considerable unpleasantness with regard to my intended marriage the result of which has been that the engagement is broken off. The matter has caused me a good deal of distress from which however I have now nearly recovered.

I am My dear Sir Benjamin

Yours very truly

Wm Odling

Brodie accepted the invitation for the following year when, such was the advance publicity whipped up by Crookes's *Chemical News*,[27] the larger rooms of the Royal Society had to be borrowed for the occasion.

Brodie, who was on intimate terms with Odling, sent him a draft of the Ideal Chemistry lecture for approval. In the following note Odling gives the first signs of his own difficulties, (i) the hypothesis that α, hydrogen, is undistributed, and (ii) the apparent prediction of the system that many of the so-called elements are 'hydrides.'

3. FROM W. ODLING   LONDON 1867[28]

January 15th [1867]
St. Bartholomew's

My dear Sir Benjamin,

I am unexpectedly called upon to lecture out of my turn for Prof Max Müller at the Royal Institution on Friday week, and have consequently been obliged to postpone my criticism on caprice[29] chemistry of //the appointment for// which I will give you full notice after my lecture, if that will be time enough I shall be glad to give your M.S. which arrived today full consideration and let you know the results. At the time your paper was under reference I had a good deal of talk and some correspondence with Stokes on the subject and am glad to know that he has acquainted you with his views.

The fundamental hypothesis is my chief—I might say my only difficulty. I admit all that you urge in your paper and have said in your letters to me in its favour, but I am unbalanced by its consequences. You make a hypothesis which accounts for the facts explained by the atomic theory, and for an equally important set of facts unexplained by it, but this by no means it seems to me necessitates the existence of a set of facts not hitherto observed, or rendered probable by observation. But I will say more when I have read your bulky notes.

Yours very truly,

W. Odling

Sir B. C. Brodie

The extent to which Brodie was advised by professional mathematicians of the calibre of William Donkin,[30] Augustus De Morgan,[31] and Henry Smith,[32] can only be appreciated from this collection. At the same time it appears that as a mathematician working in the field of the calculus of operations, Brodie was their equal, or at least well able to fend for himself. Donkin clearly rated his mathematical ability quite highly. Therefore, it appears that Brodie developed the mathematics of the Calculus *without* the aid of professional mathematicians who were only brought in to vet his technique.

De Morgan, the logician who independently of Boole had developed a logical algebra, and worked on the calculus of operations, received a copy of the first part of Brodie's Calculus in May 1867. Immediately impressed, he began a correspondence with Brodie.

4. FROM A. DE MORGAN   LONDON 1867

91 Adelaide Road NW
May 11/67

Dear Sir,

I owe you many thanks for a copy of your paper on the Chemical Calculus. I have long been looking out for an attempt at a calcular distinction between aggregation and combination.

I am desirous of making a remark upon the fundamental points; but I cannot do it until I have information upon the following point.

The paper shows an alchemist who is strong and practiced in the calcular and functional notions of algebra, but there is no allusion, so far as I can find, to the forms of the Differential Calculus. This may arise from the absence of any feeling of necessity for the Diff. Calc.; and from the power shown over algebra, it would be suspected that the author is also versed in that calculus. But on the other hand, it may be that the paper is the work of a person who has been attracted specially to *algebra* by the wants of his pursuit, and has never attended at all to the Diff. Calc.

If you will tell me how the matter stands, I will propound my comment, which I cannot do without knowing to what extent I may speak of the Diff. Calc.

I am yours faithfully,

De Morgan

Unknown to De Morgan, Brodie had graduated as a mathematician from Balliol College.[33] His confident reply is to be found in the University of London library.[34]

5. TO A. DE MORGAN   OXFORD 1867

May 12 1867
Cowley House
Oxford

My mathematical achievements are, I regret to say, only very moderate. However I have formerly studied the differential calculus, both in its principles and applications, and at one time had a very fair acquaintance with the subject, but my attention has, of late years been so entirely directed into other channels that I have much lost ground to recover. Nevertheless I might possibly appreciate any remarks, which you might be good enough to make, which did not require in their comprehension more than elementary knowledge.

In the next [paper] part of the paper I shall have occasion to consider in connection with the properties of chemical equations, what may be termed the expansion or *development* of chemical functions and it is here, I imagine, that the forms of the differential calculus, considered as a method of development, will find their application. My ideas, however, on this point, are not yet sufficiently mature to be worthy of your criticism.

I am, dear Sir,

very truly yours,

B. C. Brodie

Prof. A. De Morgan

De Morgan's elaborate reply is notable for its attack upon the fundamental equation which Brodie had introduced into the first part of the Calculus, $xy = x + y$.

6. FROM A. DE MORGAN   LONDON 1867

91 Adelaide Road NW
May 19/76 [sic]

Dear Sir Benjamin,

The calculus on which I threatened you with remarks *is* a calculus. Such a calculus there must be, and I really believe you are in the true course.

It must also be a calculus of *operation*; that is, symbols of quantity must be acted on by symbols which do not represent quantity, but action upon quantity.

Now I believe you have got it all except the *symbol of operation* which you are tacitly using, and which you have packed into the symbol $=$, as in $xy = x + y$.

To illustrate what I mean, let us return to the mathl. calculus of operations, into which the forms of all the diff. calc. &c. are packed. The root of it is the signification of the change of x into $x + 1$, the great operation of common counting. I want to signify how ϕx becomes $\phi(x + 1)$.

Every case has it(s) own common mode of signifying this. Thus x^2 becomes $(x + 1)^2$ by the operation $(\sqrt{(\ )} + 1)^2$ since $(\sqrt{x^2} + 1)^2 = \overline{x + 1}^2$. And $[\log x]^{35}$ becomes $\log (x + 1)$ by the operation $\log (e^{(\ )} + 1)$, since $\log (x + 1) = \log (e^{\log x} + 1)$. And generally ϕx becomes $\phi(x + 1)$ by the operation $\phi(\phi^{-1}(\ ) + 1)$ where ϕ^{-1} is the ϕ-verse of ϕx, or the inverse function of ϕx. For $\phi(x + 1) = \phi(\phi^{-1}(\phi x) + 1)$.

*36 Now what we want is that, in like manner as we are permitted to signify by a any number which serves our purpose, so we may be permitted to signify by a letter, say E, any operation which we know can be performed. Let $E\phi x$ be $\phi(x + 1)$, where E is an operation to which ϕ is, as it were, diaphanous, so that $E\phi x$ means $\phi E x$ or $\phi(x + 1)$.

We find that E obeys all the rules of algebra; and that $E^h \phi x$ means $\phi(x+h)$. We immediately find the symbol of the operation of differentiation. Let $D\phi x$ be the limit of

$$\frac{\phi(x+h) - \phi x}{h} \qquad (h = 0)$$

[and] a of

$$\frac{E^h - 1}{h} \cdot \phi x$$

The limit (in algebra) is $\log E$, which is the symbol of D. Hence

$$E = e^D \qquad E^h = e^{hD}$$

$$^{37}[E^{hD}] = 1 + hD + \frac{h^2 D^2}{2} + \frac{h^3 D^3}{2 \cdot 3} + \ldots$$

or

$$\phi(x+h) = \phi x + hD\phi x + \frac{h^2}{2} D^2 \phi x + \ldots$$

which is Taylor's theorem.[38]

Now you want the change from aggregation to combination; or from $x+y$ to xy. These are unquestionably the distinctive symbols of aggrn. & comb. I have noted in several places that $x+y$ and xy, is the distinction of addn. & multn. in arithmc., of aggregn. & combn. in chemistry, of 'And be it further enacted' and 'Provided always' in an Act of Parliament. Boole and myself: simultaneously—with publication on the very same day[39]—noted it as the distinction of

Both large and white } *se*lected from the classes
and   All that is large   } *co*llected into one class
         [and] all that is white}

*36 Let L be the operation that turns $x+y$ into xy. Then $xy = L(x+y)$. It is, change x, y, &c. into $\log x$, $\log y$, &c. and then take the primitive of the result. It is then, for ϕx

$$e^{\phi \, (\log \ )} x;$$

and L must act on the letters which distinguish substances, and not on the numerical coefficients which express the numbers of atoms. Thus the aggregate

$$2x + 4y + 6z$$

which combine into

$$x^2 y^4 z^6$$

is $$x^2 y^4 z^6 = L(2x + 4y + 6z)$$

or

$$e^{2 \log x + 4 \log y + 6 \log z}$$

This change made, I dare say all the rest is entirely matter between chemist and chemist, and not between chemist and mathematician.[*36]

You may have to distinguish operation(s) by different letters for different substances. Thus in $LM(x+y)$, L may refer to x and M to y. This happens in mathl. calc. of operns.—but I cannot pronounce upon it in the chemical calculus. But I am sure of this that $xy = x+y$ cannot stand unaltered. It is not even convertible: for though Water = Oxygen × Hydrogen is certainly Oxygen + Hydrogen yet Oxygen + Hydrogen is not necessarily Water.

It will never be necessary, after rules are established, to revert to the meaning of L, or whatever letter you use. In the calculus of operations, I dare say it has never even been laid down that E is $\phi(\phi^{-1}(\ ) + 1)$.

[*36] For example, it has never, I think, been insisted on that E has a distributive relation to the subject of operation.

Thus $[E(\phi x \ldots x)]$

$$\chi x = \phi x + \psi x$$

thus $$E\chi x = E\phi x + E\psi x$$

where E has three different renderings into common symbols

$$\chi(\chi^{-1}(\ ) + 1) \qquad \phi(\phi^{-1}(\ ) + 1) \qquad \psi(\psi^{-1}(\ ) + 1)$$

The addition I speak of is imperative; $xy = x+y$ cannot last. If you do not make the augmentation, another will. I appeal to Prof. Price[40] and to Prof. Donkin, if in Oxford: and I recommend you to take counsel with both. I am strongly impressed with the idea that you have started a chemical calculus, though not chemist enough to certify the details.

H

It is well that Dalton has been taken away from the evil to come. He was much against notation;[41] and when he gave a testimonial to Graham for the chair of chemistry in Univ. Coll. it was with a protest against his adoption of the symbols.

I remain

Yours truly

De Morgan

A typical contribution from Brodie's Oxford colleague, William Donkin, is the following.

7. FROM W. F. DONKIN   OXFORD 1867[42]

Let $U=f(x, y, z, \ldots)=0$ be called a 'chemical equation,' when it is true both as to matter & space.

The following are the necessary & sufficient conditions to constitute a chemical equation: viz:

U, and all its diff. coefficients of the 1st order $\left(\dfrac{du}{dx}, \dfrac{du}{dy}, \&c.\right)$

must vanish identically when $x, y, z, \ldots$ are all put $= 1$.

These conditions may be written

$$(U)=0, \quad \left(\frac{du}{dx}\right)=0, \quad \left(\frac{du}{dy}\right)=0, \quad \&c.$$

the brackets indicating that $x, y, \ldots$ have all been put $= 1$.

In fact (U) is the number of units of space

$\left(\dfrac{du}{dx}\right)$ is the number of units of matter of the kind x;

&c.

Hence if we develope U by Taylor's theorem, after writing $1+x-1$ for x, $1+y-1$ for y &c. the terms of the orders 0 and 1 disappear, & we shall have as an *algebraic* identity

$$U=\tfrac{1}{2}\left(\frac{d^2u}{dx^2}(x-1)^2+\left(\frac{d^2u}{dxdy}\right)\right)(x-1)(y-1)\ldots$$

$$+\tfrac{1}{2}\left(\frac{d^2u}{dy^2}\right)(y-1)^2$$

$$+\frac{1}{1.2.3.}\left(\frac{d^3u}{dx^3}\right)(x-1)^3 \quad \text{terms of 3d order}$$
$$+$$
$$+ \text{terms of } n\text{th order}$$

n being the degree of the highest term.

Thus, *algebraically*, the development of U in terms of $x-1$, $y-1$, &c. is *determinate*, i.e. the coefft. of any term $(x-1)^\alpha(y-1)^\beta$ ... is a determinate number, found without any difficulty.

But *chemically* all these terms vanish of themselves. (The [two first] terms of orders o and 1 vanish identically, and the next by virtue of the chemical equations $(x-1)^2 = o$ &c.)

It appears therefore quite arbitrary to retain the terms of the 2nd order, & not those of higher orders. besides, the numerical coeffts. [are]// become also// quite arbitrary. [in this]

If U is a function of x and y only, and of the second degree, then U is algebraically resoluble into linear factors, and *only in one way*. In fact (as is shown in books on conic sections) in order that U may be resoluble into factors it is necessary & sufficient that $U, \dfrac{du}{dx}, \dfrac{du}{dy}$ shall all vanish for some one pair of values of x & y.

& when $U = o$ is a chemical equation, $x = 1, y = 1$ satisfy these conditions. hence every chemical equation of the second degree between two symbols x, y, can be (by[43] algebra alone) transformed into the form

$$(ax+by+c)(a'x+b'y+c')=0$$

but it does not follow that $a\ b\ c\ a'\ b'\ c'$ are whole numbers (nor even *real*).

If in equations which represent chemical changes these coeffts. *are* whole numbers, that is a chemical fact, not an algebraical one.

The theory of the resolution of functions of a higher degree into linear factors is very complicated. & [I see no] a chemical equation is certainly *not*, merely by virtue of the above definition, necessarily resoluble into factors, if it is of the 3d degree;

ie. //it is not resoluble[44]// *algebraically*, without making use of $x+y=xy+1$ &c.

My dear Brodie,

The above is all that occurs to me at present on the subject we were last speaking of. I am going to Windsor tomorrow, but expect to be at home again within a week.

W.F.D.

P.S. I wrote a note to De Morgan since I saw you, as on trying to remember the contents of that which you proposed to send him, I thought it would, by itself, be hardly sufficiently explanatory of what I wished to say. I have not yet had an answer.

Donkin's letter to De Morgan has been preserved in London, and it clearly reveals the extent of Brodie's mathematical originality.

8. FROM W. F. DONKIN TO A. DE MORGAN[45]   OXFORD 1867

34 Broad Street,
Oxford
May 28/67

My dear Sir,

I believe Sir B. Brodie has sent, or will send, to you a note from me to himself, expressing my state of mind, at the time when it was written, about his chemical calculus. I don't think I have altered any opinion expressed in that note. But if I remember rightly it consisted more of conclusions than of reasons. So as you proposed that he should consult me, I shall be glad to lay briefly before you a statement of the way in which I regard the calculus. The fact is that I disliked the equation $x+y=xy$ quite as much as you did, and I am sure I should never have got over it. But the whole subject appeared in a totally new light when I found that Sir B. Brodie himself never really uses it (except in the 1st part of the Memoir, where it happens to do no harm), but always the equation

$$x+y=xy+1$$

or more generally

$$mx+ny=x^m y^n+m+n-1$$

which (it being observed that x and y *cannot* have numerical values, except 1, which is then a symbol of operation & not a true *number*[46]) never leads to paradoxical results like $0 = 1 = 2 = \ldots$, & allows of all ordinary algebraical processes; it is in fact a law of combination of symbols *superadded* to the ordinary laws, and not contradicting any of them any more than

$$\left(\frac{d}{dx} + \frac{1}{x}\right)^n = \left(\frac{d}{dx}\right)^n + \frac{n}{x}\left(\frac{d}{dx}\right)^{n-1}$$

does so—the cases are not properly analogous—but the latter theorem illustrates the fact that you must not give numerical values to symbols (without proper licence first had & obtained), by the absurdity of putting $\frac{d}{dx} = 2$, etc.

The question then comes what does $x + y = xy + 1$ mean, & how do we first get at it. To this my answer is as follows—and I think Sir B. Brodie accepts it as a substantially fair account of the principles of his method.

Chemical substances are conceived as existing in a gaseous state, under certain standard conditions of pressure & temperature. Then it is known, or at all events assumed, that every simple substance X can exist with densities which (if there are more than one) are multiples of some one density which may be called the primitive density of that body. We may denote by X_1, X_2, . . . the same substance X, existing with primitive density, twice primitive density, &c. Similarly for any other bodies Y, Z, &c.

Now let x [mean the operation of causing space] be the symbol of an operation performed upon space, viz.: that of causing it to be occupied by X_1; then x^2 will cause it to be occupied by X_2, and so on. xy will cause it to be occupied by X_1 and *also* by Y_1.

Let the *unit* of space be always the subject of operation. Then denoting it by a, xa will symbolize a unit of space occupied by X_1, &c.

Let $+$ mean *and*; so that $xa + ya$ will mean a unit of space full of X_1 and *another* unit full of Y_1. And $2xa$ will mean two units of space filled with X_1, whilst x^2a will mean *one* unit of space filled with X_2, ie. the *same matter* as $2xa$ . . . & so on.

Now Brodie's equation

$$xa + ya = xya$$

is true in this sense, that the *matter* on both sides is the same; but the *space* is not the same.

But if we amend it by writing

$$xa + ya = xya + a$$

it is true *both as to matter and space*—thus

"A unit of space filled with X_1
and a unit ——————————— Y_1
= a unit filled with *both* X_1 and Y_1 + an empty unit."

This amendment, which imposes on chemical equations the duty of being true *both* as to matter & space, sets the calculus on its feet. Leaving out the *subject* we get $x + y = xy + 1$.

The amendment is in no way *mine*, but Brodie's own; and all that I have done is to urge him to adopt it *ab initio*, & throw away $x + y = xy$ altogether.

I do not think the amended equation would be improved by writing $L(x+y) = xy + 1$; for I cannot find that it will ever get into difficulties as it is.

Brodie's paradoxical equations $0 = 1 = 2 = \ldots$ merely mean that any number of units of empty space contain the same matter, viz: none at all. They are true *as to matter*, but not as to space. You can extract no such paradoxes out of $x + y = xy + 1$, if you remember that x may $= 1$ (for you may take empty space as it is), but can no more $= 2$ than $\frac{d}{dx}$ can. The interpretation of $-$ leads to no more difficulty than in arithmetic. I believe that *chemical equations* possess interesting properties, but the development of them belongs to Brodie.

Believe me yours very sincerely,

W. F. Donkin

P.S. a propos of $3 = 4$, a working man (a builder's foreman) was telling my wife a few days ago how his wife, her baby (a girl), and her //the wife's// mother, all died within two days; and he added "So you might say there was *four corpses* in one house, *two mothers and two daughters.*"

Meanwhile Brodie had also written to explain to De Morgan how the equation $x + y = xy$ was transformed or normalized, into $x + y = xy + 1$.

9. TO A. DE MORGAN[47]   OXFORD 1867

Cowley House
Oxford
May 28 1867

Dear Sir,

The equation $xy = x + y$ although strictly true is nearly useless for analytical purposes, for we are not justified in performing upon it the operation of algebraic multiplication & division, and the only processes applicable to such equations are the processes of addition & substraction.[48] But the very next step which I am about to take is the transformation of this equation into the equivalent form $1 + xy = x + y$. It is this transformation which finally constitutes the Calculus, by bringing the equations under the domain of algebra.

This transformation is effected, not by the introduction of any new principle, but by combining the distributive law with the law given in the fundamental equation. From the distributive property we have

$$(x - x_1)(y - y_1) = xy + x_1 y_1 - x_1 y - xy_1$$

and eliminating by means of the equations

$$xy = x + y$$
$$x_1 y_1 = x_1 + y_1$$
$$\dots\dots\dots\dots$$
$$x_1 y = x_1 + y$$
$$xy_1 = x + y_1$$

we arrive at the equation $(x - x_1)(v - y_1) = 0$.

This is simply a new form of the fundamental equation, which is here reconciled with the distributive law.

Putting $x_1 = 1, y_1 = 1$

we have

$$(x-1)(y-1) = 0$$

and

$$1 + xy = x + y$$

the equation is now not only analytically perfect,[49] but is also interpretable. The main point to be considered //(in some way or another)// (& here I quite agree with you) is how $1 + xy$ becomes $x + y$. Of this we are informed through the factors of the equation which tell us that the operation (or event) symbolized may take place in *two* ways by the exchange of x for 1, and also by the exchange of y for 1. In other words by the transference of x and by the transference of y; which is obviously true. We hence arrive, through the Calculus, not only at a definite view as to the nature of matter, but also at a just & exact conception of the nature of the chemical process,[50] which is here to be regarded as consisting in a series of exchanges or transferences of the nature indicated by the fundamental equation when brought to its true analytical form

$$a(x-1)(y-1) = 0$$

where a indicates the *constant* in the exchange specified. Every chemical equation may be implicitly reduced to this fundamental form. These are the properties of equations, of which I propose to treat of in the second part of the Paper.

[51] I have *fully* discussed all this with Professor Donkin, and send you, with his permission, a note explaining his conclusions.

The first part of the Paper only contains the elementary principles of the method so far as necessary to the construction of the symbols through the equations. The form of the equation there given $xy = x + y$ is sufficient for that purpose. I am as unwilling to crab away[52] the question with unnecessary matter. But I am sure, from Donkin's remark, that I had better at once have given the transformation referred to.

Very faithfully yours

B. C. Brodie

Prof. De Morgan

The version actually received by De Morgan (preserved at London) closes with two slightly different paragraphs.

As this change in the form of the equation is not mentioned, you really have not had the system fully put before you. The equation $xy = x + y$ is utterly futile and will never appear again upon the scene. It was necessary to make some division of the subject, and rightly or wrongly I drew the line here.

I have fully explained all this to Donkin to whom also I submitted your letter. I send to you with his permission a note explaining his view of the question.

I am dear Sir,

Very faithfully yours,

B. C. Brodie

The enclosure mentioned by Brodie, a letter from Donkin, has been preserved in the De Morgan collection.

10. FROM W. F. DONKIN[53]   OXFORD? 1867

My dear Brodie,

Thanks for your letter. I don't quite see some of the things you say about my M. But it does not signify. Because I now see that in order that you may use your calculus safely it is only necessary that every chemical equation shall be true separately with respect to *matter* and *space*. That is, supposing an equation

$$nx^{\alpha}y^{\beta} \ldots + n'x'^{\alpha'}y^{\beta'} + \ldots = 0$$

in order that it may be allowable to use it without reserve, not only the whole *matter* (of each kind) must be zero, but the *whole space* also. ie. you must have

<table>
<tr><td>besides</td><td>

$n + n' + n'' + \ldots = 0$
$n\alpha + n'\alpha' + \ldots = 0$
$n\beta + n'\beta' + \ldots = 0$
$\ldots\ldots\ldots\ldots$&c.

</td></tr>
</table>

I believe you have told me all this before. But I certainly did not see that these conditions are *necessary & sufficient* to enable you to use all the ordinary processes of algebra; to which you super-add the peculiar & characteristic transformation of your system viz:

$$mx + ny = x^m y^n + m + n - 1$$

This being the case I certainly should not advise any change in the notation. Tho' it may be matter for consideration how far the principles of the method may be capable of being expanded in a manner more likely to recommend it to mathematicians.

I think it is almost impossible for any reader to understand the system as it appears in your first part, without such help as I have had from you. The change of $x + y = xy$ into $x + y = xy + 1$ is not optional, but absolutely essential.

Yours sincerely,

W. F. Donkin

Friday May 24 [1867]

However, University examinations left De Morgan with neither time to digest either Brodie's or Donkin's remarks, nor unfortunately time to attend Brodie's Ideal Chemistry lecture.[54]

11. FROM A. DE MORGAN   LONDON 1867

91 Adelaide Road NW

June 5/67

My dear Sir Benjamin,

I had hoped to have got down to the Chemical Socy. tomorrow,[55] when I should have talked to you about your note, and one from Prof. Donkin,[56] which is new exposition. But examination papers have come between—*verbum sapiente*, when the sage is a Univy. Profr. I must defer it all until towards the end of the month.

Yours truly

De Morgan

Sir B. Brodie Bt.

Unfortunately for Brodie, Donkin died in 1869, and De Morgan in 1871; he was therefore robbed of the stimulus and propaganda which they might have provided for Part II.[57] From the following letter, however, it would appear that the role of mathematical adviser was assumed instead by another colleague and close friend, Henry Smith.

Simultaneously with the publication of Part II of the Calculus in 1877, Brodie produced a strange paper 'On the relative "Facility of Production" of Chemical Combination' in which he used probability theory to effect 'a comparison between the hydrocarbons actually produced and their relative "facility of production" as indicated by theory.'[58] The map referred to was based on the Arithmetic Triangle of Pascal, and Brodie claimed that the resulting plots vindicated his Calculus.

12. FROM H. J. S. SMITH[59]   OXFORD 1877?

University Museum,
Oxford

Dear Brodie,

I think your paper, and map, are perfectly clear; and I think also that you have avoided all mathematical traps, gins, and pitfalls, with distinguished success.

Perhaps it might be as well to state, with more clearness than you have done, that in this paper you only compare the 'facility of production' of bodies upon the same base line.[60] *e.g.* you do not attempt to compare the 'facility of production' of $a^5\kappa^5$ and $a^5\kappa^6$. I have spent some time (without any success) in considering whether your principal might not be extended so as to cover cases of this kind. If it had not been for this, I could have returned your paper much sooner. At the end of p. 9 I would suggest that the words 'great paramount cause' are a little too strong.[61] The map does certainly suggest //that there must be// some cause for increased facility of production above it.

I am so glad to hear that you are going abroad. It is a clear proof that you must have gained enormously in health and strength.

Ever very truly yours
Henry S. Smith

One interesting aspect of the reception accorded to Brodie's Calculus is the 'coverage' given to it by Crookes's *Chemical News* and John Cargill Brough's ill-fated *Laboratory*.[62] During 1867, the latter published two letters from the logician William Stanley Jevons criticizing the Calculus; and a reply from Brodie. The background to this public dispute is revealed in three private letters of Jevons to Brodie. Jevons[63] had not only studied chemistry under the atomic realist, Williamson, but he was also a cousin of Brodie's personal friend, Henry Roscoe, who was one of the first chemists to utilize physical evidence for the atomic theory. Jevons, not surprisingly, was therefore a firm believer in atoms. He could have been a formidable critic of Brodie's system for, ironically, he had also studied mathematics with no less a person than De Morgan, and he had just become known for his adaptation of Boolean logic.[64] No doubt this prompted Brodie to send him a copy of Part I of the Calculus, but Jevons's reaction can hardly have been quite what Brodie expected.

13. FROM W. S. JEVONS   MANCHESTER 1867

9 Birch Grove
Rusholme
Manchester
25 May 1867

Dear Sir,

I beg to thank you for your kindness in forewarding me a copy of your paper on the Chemical Calculus. I had however had the pleasure of reading it in another copy, and felt much interest in the subject. I am truly sorry that I cannot feel convinced of the truth of all your views. So strongly indeed do I feel the insecurity of your fundamental equation that I have been led to write a few remarks on this point.

I have written them in the form of a communication to the Philosophical Magazine, but I much prefer in the first place to submit them directly to your consideration. I have therefore, posted you the M.S. hoping that you will excuse the liberty of criticism of which I have evailed myself.[65]

I beg that you will deal with my remarks just as you think fit. But you will doubtless desire that the truth of your system should be freely tested and if as is most probable, you consider your position unshaken by my objections, I presume that you would rather desire their publication than not.

I beg to remain Dear Sir

Yours very faithfully

W. S. Jevons

Sir B. C. Brodie Bart.

Brodie clearly lost no time in showing Jevons's criticism to Donkin who advised as follows.

14. FROM W. F. DONKIN   OXFORD 1867[66]

34 Broad Street
Oxford

My Dear Brodie,

I really think you ought to persuade Jevons, if you can, to defer his publication at least until he has seen what more you have to say. He will do no discredit to himself, and I fear injury to you. The unmathematical world (including chemists) will think he has refuted your system. Any mathematician will see at a glance that whatever objection there may or may not be to $xy = x + y$, at all events Mr Jevons has not found it out. I never saw a weaker production. His objection to xy shows that either he totally misunderstands what you mean by it, or that he does not know what a calculus of operations really is, or more probably both. What possible difficulty is there in conceiving different portions of matter successively put into the same space.

The comparison of $\qquad xy = x + y$

with $\qquad\qquad\quad 2^2 = 2 + 2$

is mere nonsense. You cannot put $x = 2$ any more than you might put $\dfrac{d}{dx} = 2$. The only thing of the kind you *can* do is to reduce x^n to 1 by putting $n = 0$. n is a numerical symbol, but x is not. Putting $n = 0$ implies that you don't perform the operation x at all—you leave the subject as it is—which is the operation 1.

It is proved in the Diff. Calc.: considered as a calculus of operations, that

$$\left(\frac{d}{dx}+\frac{1}{x}\right)^n = \left(\frac{d}{dx}\right)^n + \frac{n}{x}\frac{d}{dx}$$

but you cannot put $\frac{d}{dx}=1$, or 2, or any other number without getting an absurd result. In the formula of your calculus

$$nx + 1 = x^n + n$$

you can get a true result by putting $n=0$, but not by putting $x=2$.

$$[** \ldots **]$$

Here however you and I begin in a certain sense to differ, because you will say that

$$2n + 1 = 2^n + n \quad \textit{is} \text{ true.}$$

However this may be, it cannot possibly be maintained that all symbols in a calculus of operations ought to be replaceable by *numbers*. Mr Jevons has no conception of the real nature of the questions raised by $x+y=xy$, & it would probably be hopeless to try to enlighten him. Therefore if possible let him be prevented from meddling.

Ever yours

W.F.D.

see over

P.S. I ought to have made an exception in favour of putting $x=1$; because you may make x refer to that kind of matter which is identical with empty space. Still 1 is the *operation* 1, not the *number* 1. And I don't see any conceivable meaning for $x=2$.

Brodie framed his reply to Jevons as diplomatically as possible.

15. TO W. S. JEVONS[67]   OXFORD 1867

Cowley House
Oxford
May 27 1867

Dear Sir,

I thank you for your consideration in forewarding to me the copy of your criticism before publication.

You do not of course expect me to admit the validity of your objections, which, I must candidly say, appear to me to rest partly on an imperfect comprehension of my statement but still more on an inadequate appreciation (at least according to my ideas) of the general principles of algebraic reasoning and expression. As I have already given my opinion very fully upon these points which you raise I really do not think that anything would be gained by a further discussion of the subject on my part, and I must leave your remarks to the consideration of those who are competent to form an [*opinion*] judgement upon them.

As you have been good enough to apprise me of your intention it is only fair to you to inform you that I hope before long to publish a short abstract of the way in which I propose to proceed to the treatment of the equation, which [is calculated to] perhaps might modify your ideas (and certainly ought to modify some of your statements) in regard to the calculus considered as an [mathematical] analytical method.

Faithfully yours

B. C. Brodie

Prof. W. Jevons

Brodie's promise of a clarificatory article in the near future seems to have mollified Jevons—at any rate, his article was never published in the *Philosophical Magazine*.

16. FROM W. S. JEVONS   MANCHESTER 1867

> 9 Birch Grove
> Rusholme
> 29 May 1867

Dear Sir,

   I am very much obliged to you for replying to my letter. You may rely upon it that I shall carefully consider the subject many times over before venturing to print anything upon it, & if I discover any reason at all to suppose my criticism unfounded, I should at once apologise for having troubled you at all on the subject.

   My objections you will have noticed do not bear against the employment of systems of equations in chemistry, which I should perfectly agree with you must form the basis of chemistry as of every other exact science, but against the special condition

$$xy = x + y$$

But I have no desire whatsoever to enter into a personal discussion of the subject, & I will take time to consider before saying more about it.

> Believe me Dear Sir
>
> Yours very faithfully
>
> W. S. Jevons

Sir B. C. Brodie Bart.

However, Jevons proceeded to have second thoughts, and perhaps prompted by the reports of Brodie's clarificatory lecture in *Laboratory*,[68] he sent Brough a critical letter which was published in the week of 22 June.[69] To Brough's delight (for 'big' names could be used to promote the sale of his luckless journal) Brodie replied pinpointing the nature of Jevons's misunderstanding.[70] But Jevons was not outwitted, and in a further communication he shifted his ground to a far more pertinent criticism of Brodie's use of commutative algebra.[71] Brodie made no public reply to this, probably because almost immediately after his June lecture he fell seriously ill. Thereafter he was never completely free from sickness and this led to his early retirement, and the incompleteness of his system.

Williamson, who was a competent mathematician (it should be remembered that he had studied with Comte), translated Brodie's symbols into traditional notation for the Royal Society on 20 June 1867.[72] In the following letter he reveals that this note was only part of a longer paper which he intended to write.[73] I believe that this paper became the famous Presidential Address to the Chemical Society of 1869, 'On the Atomic Theory'. If this is the case, it is ironic that Williamson should have ignored Brodie's Calculus in this defence of atomism.

17. FROM A. W. WILLIAMSON   LONDON 1867

Univ. Coll.
19 June [1867]

My dear Brodie,

I wrote the greater part of a letter to you on Friday last saying that I could not go down to see you on Saturday and giving an outline of the remarks which I then intended to bring forward a propos of your memoir. An interruption prevented me from finishing the letter—and I am ashamed to say that instead of writing you two lines which I might have done I waited for leisure to finish my remarks intelligibly.

What I have to say proves to be far too much for the present occasion. I need hardly say that its tenor is positive[74] not negative and I shall put it together with some care. Meanwhile I propose giving a note at the R.S. tomorrow chiefly relating to the choice between volumes & weights as the basis of a calculus. Your proposal of a change of theory in the atomic constitution of hydrogen (and)[75] chlorine I own must of course be judged as a whole.[76] My business relates mainly to considerations relating to the prevailing system as a *whole*. I should have been very sorry if you had come up at any risk to your health—but shall be glad when you can come up * *.

I heard on Monday that in the next number of the Philosophical Magazine there is to be an article hostile to your views

I

but by whom I do not know.[77] I do not even know whether the author is competent to treat the subject.

Yours sincerely

Alex. A. Williamson

Meanwhile, Brodie had sent an offprint of Part I to the astronomer and Grand Old Man of British science, Sir John Herschel, who had discussed the need for an improved chemical notation on several occasions.[78] If, as seems likely, Brodie began his serious search for a new notation on the basis of Herschel's critical remarks[79] at the British Association in 1858, he must have been bitterly disappointed at the conservative nature of Herschel's reaction to the notation of the Calculus.

18. FROM SIR JOHN HERSCHEL   COLLINGWOOD 1867

Collingwood
May 4 1867

Sir,

I beg to return you my best thanks for the very interesting volume you have been so good as to send me on the 'Calculus of Chemical Operations' which I shall read with much attention as it seems from the glimpse I have got of it on a first inspection likely to embody in a systematised manner the principal amount of progress which has hitherto been made in that department of science.

I have the honour to remain

Yours very truly

J. F. W. Herschel

19. TO SIR JOHN HERSCHEL[80]   OXFORD 1867

May 24, 1867
Cowley House,
Oxford

Sir,

As you have been so good as to say that you intended to read my Paper with attention I should esteem it a great kindness if you would communicate to me any critical remarks upon the principles of the method which occurs to you. I should especially like to know whether you are induced to take objection to the equation $xy = x + y$. As if so, I should wish to have an opportunity of explaining to you the way in which I propose to deal with this equation.

My excuse for troubling you must be that if these notions are ever to penetrate to the chemical public it must be through the intervention of those few persons who from the familiarity with the whole subject, both mathematically and chemically considered, are competent to pass a judgement upon them.

I am Sir

Very faithfully yours

B. C. Brodie

Sir J. Herschel

20. FROM SIR JOHN HERSCHEL[81]   COLLINGWOOD 1867

Collingwood

June 13 1867

Dear Sir,

I have to apologise for not earlier replying to yours of the 24th. ult.—but besides that I have been much occupied, your book takes *a* [*great*] *good deal of reading* and in fact very much more than I have yet been able to give it so that I cannot be at all sure that I have seized the spirit of the *very abstract* way in which you [represent] present the system. Neither am I sufficiently conversant with the latter advances [in] of chemistry to know whether the result arrived at in respect of Chlorine Bromine &c.—(viz. that they are not in reality simple bodies but compounds of one—what shall I say—monad?—of hydrogen with 2 monads of an *unknown* body (ξ or β &c. as the case may be) [*one*] *each* of which with 1 monad of hydrogen gives the *known bodies* muriatic, hydrobromic &c acids—(in other words that chlorine is a compound of muriatic acid with an unknown element)—whether, (I say) this be a received theory,—or a new result, arrived at thus symbolically by yourself, and awaiting its confirmation by future experiments.

Your question however goes only to the point of a notation— & especially the point whether $x + y = xy$ is to be regarded as objectionable? I must confess I think it a fatal objection to any system of notation when it runs so contrary to the conventions of a very widely diffused & [thoroughly] strongly established system received on another subject and whose elements it employs, as to raise between two great classes of thinkers (between whom it is desirable that there should be a perfect interchange of ideas) an almost insuperable barrier—just that sort of barrier which the good Greek Bishop who gave the Russians their alphabet raised between them & all the European nations by affixing to the Greek letters Russian meanings corresponding to the *sounds* of totally different Greek characters. Of course if some great object (distinct from the mere convenience of a short-hand) is to be gained by so doing—one which could not be, or not without [great] some difficulty, otherwise accomplished—there would be nothing to be said but so far as I see this is not the case. All your equations & reasonings—so far as I have gone into them, may with perfect readiness (& to my mind with *far greater distinctness*—as relieving the mind from the perpetual risk of mistake) be put into the ordinary algebraic notation. Thus I should write your equation

$$2a^m\xi^{m_1} = 2a + a^n\xi^{n_1}$$

thus

$$[2(ma + m_1\xi) = 2a + a^n\xi^{n_1}]$$

$$2(ma + m_1\xi) = 2a + (na + n_1\xi)$$

and I should then gain this advantage that every reader who understood algebra would see its truth whereas thousands of such readers would demur at the other form.

Moreover, in such equations as this your numerical element 2 is used in its algebraic *not* its chemical sense—(according to which $2a^m\xi^{m_1}$ would mean $2 + ma + m_1\xi$) as a mere coefficient. This may be perhaps held unobjectionable—but how? [where] when *a letter* as x or t takes its place as in your equation p. 828

$$ya^mx^{m_1} = 2ya + xa^nx^{n_1}?$$

which chemically interpreted into algebraic language ought to be equivalent to

$$y + ma + m_1x = 2(y + a) + (x + na + n_1x)$$

not

$$mya + m_1yx = 2ya + nxa + n_1xx$$

It may perhaps be said that italic letters are to denote bona fide numerical coefficients & Greek letters chemical symbols—but there are 60 or 70 chemical elements (each requiring a letter) and both greek & roman & italic letters will be used up in the requirements of this system—besides which it [cannot] // must // be held very objectionable, in a system where letters stand for ideas—that one set of letters should be manipulated according to one convention and another according to another. Take for instance your equation p. 835, 836.

$$2y_1 a^m \chi^{m_1} \beta_1^{m_2} = 3 y_1 a \chi^2 + y_2 a^n \chi^{n_1} \beta_1^{n_2}$$

and
$$\frac{y_2 w}{2y_1} = 5\cdot5 \qquad y_2 = 1 + 2z$$

To one ignorant of algebra I can conceive such equations, early instilled as *chemical notation*, to have become familiar & manageable—but an algebraist would always feel *not at home* and liable to continual mistakes in their management & would be compelled to translate them into his own language to use them safely. What *can* an algebraist say to $0 = 1$?

I can conceive a certain convenience arising from brevity of writing to arise from omitting altogether the signs, $+$ and $-$ (N.B. $-$ and $\div$ can have no place in a chemical formula of composition). Thus to express the composition of [crystallized] crystalline sulphate of soda, one might write

$$\theta\xi^3 \cdot \sigma\xi^2 \cdot 10a\xi \ \text{or} \ (\theta\xi^3)(\sigma\xi^2)(10a\xi)$$

regarding the [numeral] numerical 10 as strictly a numerical coefficient and holding the mental reservation that the symbolic letters are to be regarded as antilogarithms (or exponentials) of the numbers expressing their relative atomic values. Such a system, by avoiding any violent and direct collision with algebraic convention, *might* perhaps be found useful. But after all I can imagine no sufficient reason for throwing overboard the *pure and simple* algebraic expression of absolute numerical weights & writing for instance,

$$(\theta + 3\xi) + (\sigma + 2\xi) + 10(a + \xi)$$

where the grouping speaks for itself.

I trust you will pardon me for using this freedom of expression in speaking of what is evidently a most elaborate system & must have been the result of much thought—but as you have expressed a wish to know my own impressions, I have been pleased to offer them & remain

Dear Sir

Yours very [sincerely] truly

J. F. W. Herschel

21. TO SIR JOHN HERSCHEL[82]   OXFORD 1867

Cowley House
Oxford
June 26 1867

Dear Sir,

I have been intending every day to write and thank you for the trouble you have taken in stating to me so fully your views on the subject of my Calculus, which I appreciate as a very real act of kindness. On consideration it appears to me better to postpone any further explanations on my part, until I more fully comprehend the point of your objection, as otherwise I may shoot very wide of the mark.

I cannot but think that you are under some fundamental misconception as to the meaning of my symbols, and that you are mixing up together two things, which are very distinct, namely the *operations* indicated by a and ξ, and the numbers which express the weights of the portions of matter resulting from these operations, which numbers I have called $w(a)$ and $w(\xi)$. It certainly would be a very absurd notation to write the weight of the unit of water $w(a) \times w(\xi)$. ie. 1×8, which however is what I understand to be done in the notation of atomic weights HO. The symbols a and ξ however cannot be replaced by numbers and indeed have *no numerical equivalents* whatsoever, and the whole gist of this method is that such an interpretation is assigned to these letters as not only *justifies* but absolutely *necessitates*, (if we would have any pretensions to algebraic consistency) the introduction of the symbol $a\xi$, as the symbol of the operation by which the unit of water is made. As the *spurious* introduction of such a symbol in violation of algebraic analogy, is an unmixed evil, so the *real* introduction of this symbol cannot but be fraught with the most important consequences. This system is based upon the relation which subsists between *matter* & *space*, and is intended to express the law of gaseous change. I will interprete briefly the symbol $a1 + \xi1$ and $a\xi1$.

The symbol 1 says 'Take the unit of space as it is.'

a—Perform upon that unit the operation a, of which the result is to constitute a unit of that kind of matter we call hydrogen.

$\xi1$—do the same in regard to ξ.

$a1 + \xi1$—take these *two* things together aggregated in any way that you please.

Now consider the symbol $a\xi1$. (1) getting us as before to construct the matter called ξ. & now having constituted that matter, perform *upon it* the operation a. The result of this successive performance of these operations is to constitute *one unit* of matter which contains the matter of a and also of ξ. There is a fundamental distinction in natural objects which is expressed, [by these] and I conceive properly and adequately expressed, by the algebraic distinction, $a + \xi$, and $a\xi$. But between the symbols $a + \xi$ and $(a + \xi)$, there is simply *no algebraic* distinction, and how can they be used to discriminate as to objects, between which there is a *real* distinction?

If when you have leisure you will kindly send me a line informing me *why* you consider $a\xi$ contrary to algebraic convention, I shall be better able to understand the present point of your letter. But I entirely agree with all that you say as to the necessity of conforming to algebraic proprieties, and only differ from you in *considering* that I do *in the strictest sense*, conform to the principles of algebra. That you may, *so far as I have yet gone*, follow my reasonings in * my symbols, is, I think true and for a very obvious reason, namely that to construct my symbols I do (or may) make use of the equation

$$2ma + m_1\xi = 2a + na + n_1\xi$$

and that for this construction of the symbol this equation is all that is necessary. But when we proceed further with the study of the equations you will see that this is no longer the case, and that the *distinctive* properties of the composite symbol $a\xi$ necessarily come into play. My question about $xy = x + y$ was really directed altogether to another point, namely as to the way in which we are to operate with the equation, which is not obvious, and if you had not seen how this was to be done, I should like to have explained it to you. It is quite true that if the *whole* Calculus were contained in this *first* Part, it would be of very little more *use* (although doubtless it is much more accurate and consistent) than our present method. In the face of your present objection however it is useless even to consider this question, as if it were really valid the whole method would *ipso facto* fall to the ground. I cannot however but say that I suspect that you are thinking of one thing and I of another.

I am, dear Sir

Very faithfully & respectfully yours

B. C. Brodie

Sir J. Herschel

There is no evidence that Herschel continued with this correspondence.

The atomist, August Wilhelm Hofmann, appears to have only taken a kindly interest in publicizing the Calculus in Germany for the purpose of gaining Brodie election to the Berlin Academy.[83]

22. FROM A. W. HOFMANN   BERLIN 1867

Berlin, O-* Strasse
June 26 1867

My dear Brodie,

Excuse that I send so late a reply to your note. The last days of my stay in Paris were not less busy as you may imagine than the first time after my return to Berlin. I found here the copy of your papers, which had arrived during my absence. There are three distinguished mathematicians in Berlin in addition to

Kummer,[84] all members of the Berlin Academy. viz. Prof. Kronecker,[85] Prof. Weierstrass, [86] Prof. Borchardt.[87] You should certainly send copies to these men; they are all likely to take an interest in this question more especially Kronecker who has an essentially chemical turn and who is sure to examine the paper closely, particularly so since he knows that you are intimately acquainted with Mr Henry Smith,[88] for whom he entertains a most * * respects. I am rather anxious * * for sooner or later an opportunity may present itself * * renders you as a candidate for the Berlin Academy. If you will send me the papers I shall have great pleasure in distributing them. There are several others here to whom you might transmit a copy of the papers, if you have some more to spare. Magnus,[89] Dorn,[90] G. Rose[91] and Rammelsberg,[92] lastly Buff[93] and Du Bois Raymond.[94] Of the last named only Rammelsberg is likely to take the matter up, in the case of the others it would be simply a means of attention.

It is of course with the greatest pleasure that I place another copy of the Report of the chemical laboratories at your disposal. Unfortunately I have no spare copy here, which I could as one forward. But there are many copies with Mrs Wilson my Mother in law[95] and your friend might get a copy at any moment by forewarding the enclosed card to 24 Park Square, East Regents Park, where the servant who takes care of the house during Mrs Wilson's absence has access to the books.

I met a few weeks ago Mr Sterry Hunt in Paris, who told me that he had for some time been staying with you. He gave me a tolerably grave account of your health; let me hope that another vacation will set you up entirely again.[96] It is useful to remember sometimes that we are no longer in the first prime of youth and that we should take things a little easier than formerly. I had a very decided warning last winter. An abscess had formed in my neck, which for a time rendered me perfectly unable to work. Fortunately I am perfectly right again, but I have made up my mind to work in a more leisured manner hence forth.

There is every possibility that I shall come to England in autumn and perhaps may be fortunate enough * * * * another pleasant * * with my friends in Oxford. Will you kindly remember me to Lady Brodie and believe me

My dear Brodie

Ever yours very sincerely

A. W. Hofmann

P.S. The papers you would send most conveniently in a parcel by The British and Continental Parcel Delivery Express. Have you any printed papers setting forth in a somewhat detailed manner the scientific work which you have done, a resume such as the french publish on the eve of elections under the significant title Titres de M.NN. If so would you send it to me. It might also do wonders.

A sophisticated yet sympathetic criticism of the Calculus was made by Alexander Crum Brown in August 1867.[97] He courteously explained his position to Brodie in a letter sent from Ireland where he had gone for the funeral of a member of his wife's family.[98]

23. FROM A. CRUM BROWN   PORTRUSH, IRELAND 1867

2 Strandview

Portrush Co. Antrim

Aug. 19. 1867

Dear Sir,

Since the beginning of the month, I have been so completely out of the scientific world, that I have not yet seen the Phil. Mag. I expect some copies of my remarks & when I get them shall be most happy to send you one. In writing the equations $O = 2\xi$ &c. $Cl = 2\chi\sqrt{a}$ &c. or rather (changing the unit) $O = \xi$, $Cl = \chi\sqrt{a}$ what I mean is that, apart from interpretation altogether, & looking merely at the systems from a formal point of view the symbols on the left hand are equivalent in the one system to those on the right hand in the other. Or, that giving a functional meaning to O, H, Cl &c. O is the same as ξ, H is the imaginary operation of which the square is a, Cl the imaginary operation of which the square is $a\chi^2$, or χ the imaginary operation $H^{-1}Cl$. Or that giving an atomic meaning to your symbols a is H^2, ξ is O &c. I wrote the equations however, rather as a step towards a method of translation of the one *notation* into the other, than with the view of comparing the ideas which suggested the notations. Indeed throughout the paper I wish to confine my remarks to the notation as a method of symbolizing facts, as this is all that is necessarily common to all systems of Chemical notation. The system which I should prefer, in the mean time, is not, as you put it, the a^2 system, but the system of which the fundamental hypothesis is that the *elements* (a really well marked group of substances) are simple with respect to each other, & this leads at once to a^2 & to a system *formally* the same as the one in actual use. It seems to me that we have as good grounds for this assumption as for unit of hydrogen $= a$. I should not be greatly surprized if the course of discovery shows that some, or all, of the so-called elements are compound, but I decline to represent them as compounds at present, because I do not know their compositions.

If we are guided merely by the facts at present known, & make no assumption at all, we get the symbols which I put in a footnote, Hydn. $a\nu^2$, chlorine $a\chi^2$, oxygen ξ, &c. Now the assumption $\nu = 1$ seems as arbitrary (if not more so) as $a = 1$.[99]

As to the distributive law, I am not convinced, but am quite open to conviction. I have no difficulty as to the chem. symbol 1, but 2, 3 &c. are so connected with the distributive law that the objection I have to it extend to them.

As I said, I have not attempted to criticise the *ideas* which suggest your notation. The idea of functional relation between substances, is, I think, a very happy one. It had occurred to me myself, whether spontaneously or from some forgotten intimation of what you were doing I cannot tell, at all events I have developed it in a totally different way & with nothing like the same completeness. My paper is in the press just now and when it appears I shall send you a copy.

I am Yrs very truly

Alexr Crum Brown

Crum Brown's own 'atomic' mathematical system had been read to the Royal Society of Edinburgh on 18 February 1867.

He noted in the published version[100] that it differed from Brodie's Calculus 'in method, object, and result,' for it had not been designed to replace the usual notation, but 'to express certain general and serial relations in those cases where the common atomic notation is inconvenient or obscure.' The system was nevertheless an operational calculus.

It seems likely that Crum Brown's application of mathematics to chemistry, which he did not extend, caught the imagination of two brilliant London mathematicians who were interested in chemistry: Arthur Cayley and William Sylvester. Cayley developed a mathematical theory of isomers (or 'trees'),[101] while Sylvester created a 'Chemical Algebra' which continued to stimulate the theory of invariants until about 1905, and which has been recognized by Weyl as a forerunner of Quantum Mechanics.[102]

By August 1867 it would have become clear to Brodie that the most telling criticism of his Calculus was aimed at the apparently arbitrary way he preferred the a (1-volume) system as opposed to the a^2 (2-volume) system which had the advantage of symmetry with the existing Berzelian nomenclature. But at this period he does not appear to have been able to justify it. Later, in Part II of the Calculus, he claimed that the assumption that hydrogen was undistributed (a) was in accord with the law of even numbers. Since the a^2 system was not, the former was the preferred system.

In the following letter Odling referred to the forthcoming challenge of the British Association meeting at Dundee.

24. FROM W. ODLING   CROYDON 1867

Croydon
August 11th. 1867

My dear Sir Benjamin,

I am glad to hear that you are in the country and I trust enjoying the sea-breezes[103] regardless of the polemical breezes blowing at you from all sides. I agree that your opponents do not make out much of a case and I certainly should not trouble myself about their individual attacks, which are of the kind which every one must expect who rightly or wrongly traverses old established notions or habits. I think however it might be well for both sides if you would bring out more defending your reasons for preferring the system of a to that of a^2. Herewith I forward you Crum Brown's paper[97]—I sent myself a reply to Wanklyn's insolence[77] but after hearing from you and on second thoughts wrote to Francis[104] to withdraw it. When I get the copy back from him I will send it you for perusal.

I have to give the introductory lecture this year at St. Bartholomews,[105] the preparation for which is giving me a good deal of trouble but if I find that I can afford the time I shall go to Dundee, in which case if you do not object I will bring the subject of your chemical calculus before the notice of Section B. Crum Brown and all the Scotchmen I suppose except Playfair[106] will be there. Trusting that you will soon feel yourself again advising you not to trouble yourself about these matters at any rate for the present.

I am

Yours very truly,

W. Odling

Odling was able to attend the Dundee meeting, but he did not have to raise the subject of the Calculus for it was immediately placed on the agenda by Thomas Anderson in his Presidential Address[107] to Section B, and by Crum Brown during the week's proceedings.[108] The Assistant General Secretary of the British Association, George Griffiths, sent Brodie a short account of the discussion which followed Crum Brown's paper.

25. FROM G. GRIFFITHS   HARROW 1867

British Association for the Advancement of Science
Thirty-Seventh Meeting—Dundee, 1867

Harrow
14 Sep. 1867

My dear Brodie,

I desired the publisher of the Dundee Advertiser to forward to you copies of his newspaper which has given by far the best account of our proceedings.[109]

There was a good discussion of your Calculus of Chemical Operations. I fortunately knew on Saturday that Dr Crum Brown was to bring it before Section B on Monday and at St Andrews on Saturday evening I met Prof. Harley[110] & told him of it. He however unfortunately did not know anything about your paper and I was able to give him but little information sitting at dinner with 150 persons all talking at the same time. On Monday morning someone seems to have lent him some papers relating to the subject,[111] but not your original paper. I had time to hear Dr Brown's paper which was little more than a reproduction of his paper in the Philosophical Magazine. Maxwell called on by the President, just made a few remarks, not however, of much importance.[112] Mr. Harley then spoke at considerable length & explained how he differed from Dr Crum Brown in many points & stated that he thoroughly approved of your attempt to do for Chemistry what Boole did for Logic, & after explaining what Boole did he showed what seemed to be unfinished in your work. He referred to Boole's Law of duality $x^n = x$ as being the condition under which the ordinary processes of algebra are applicable to logic, in the same manner he said that there might be an analogous condition in the calculus of chemical operations which he explained at length. & he further pointed out that Mr Jevons in his letter[69, 71] to you had made the same error as he had done in his logic in reference to Boole's system. I was then obliged to leave the room but I believe that the discussion was continued for some time afterwards. Of course the newspapers could not give any report of such discussion as this. Mr Harley told me that he would send you what he had written about Boole's logic in the British Quarterly Review.[113] His address is The Manse, Brighouse, Yorkshire. (or Airedale College, Bradford.) I hope that Lady Brodie & all your family are very well.

Very truly yours

G. Griffiths

In the 'exceedingly animated discussion' at Dundee, the participants were Maxwell, Harley, Odling, Williamson, A. R. Catton and J. A. Wanklyn. Catton expressed admiration for

Brodie's mathematical skill while Wanklyn complained that Crum Brown had stolen his criticisms from Davey and himself. The latter irrelevancy was decently buried by Odling who went on to defend Brodie. 'The professor concluded a long and very interesting discussion, by speaking of notations as being only tools which must be tested by actual experiment, and saying that it was not enough that they should express known facts, that they must also lead to unknown and unexplored fields of inquiry. He regretted the present fragmentary character of Sir B. Brodie's work, which might, if completed, be less liable to some of the objections raised against it.'[109]

Perhaps the most intriguing aspect of Griffith's report is the rapid way in which the logician Robert Harley familiarized himself with the Calculus—literally overnight, and the energetic manner in which he defended it. Brodie promptly sent Harley an offprint and received this reply.

26. FROM REV. R. H. HARLEY   BRIGHOUSE 1867

The Manse
Brighouse. Yorks.
Oct. 31, 1867

Dear Sir B. Brodie,

I thank you very much for sending me a copy of your very remarkable memoir on the calculus of chemical operations. It is to me matter of much regret that I am not at present in a condition to examine the subject with that degree of care & attention which it so richly merits. During the late meeting of the British Assn. at Dundee, however, I heard & read enough to satisfy me that your researches are of high speculative impact, & possibly also of great practical value. I am chiefly interested in them because of their obvious connexion with Boole's logical system: & I am very curious to see how you will construct an Algebra in which the symbols x, y, &c. obey all the rules of common Algebra & yet are subject to the chemical law expressed by $xy = x + y$.

So long as my professional duties at Brighouse & Bradford continue as numerous & exacting as they are at present, I cannot hope to be able to read such profound Papers as yours, or indeed to go deeply into any subject. But I am living in hope that I may some day get into a position in wh. I shall be able to give more time to scientific studies. You will see by the accompanying Application that I am a candidate for the Chair formerly held by Boole at Cork. Such a post would exactly suit me, but I fear that I am not likely to get it—I have no friends at Court.—Be pleased to accept a copy of an essay[113] on Boole which I wrote last year amid many interruptions: some parts of it may possibly interest you. Again thanking you I am,

Dear Sir Benjamin Brodie,

Yours respectfully,

R. H. Harley

There are no indications, however, that Harley took any further interest in Brodie's Calculus.

One of the more outlandish participants in the aftermath to the Williamson debate on atomism in 1869 was the chemical engineer and mathematician, William Henry Walenn.[114] Three letters of his written to Brodie in 1867 confirm the impression that he was a disciple of Brodie's. His analysis of other chemists' reactions to the Calculus is acute.

27. FROM W. H. WALENN[115]   LONDON 1867

19 Talbot Road
Tufnell Park West,
London, N.
Nov. 6, 1867

Sir,

This day I forward to you No. 3 of the Quarterly Journal of Education for your acceptance; it contains an article of mine upon 'Chemical Notation.'

Occupation of time has hitherto prevented me from entering fully upon your Calculus. I do not consider that I have done more than introduced the subject in its most popular form, and taken the matter of symbols up from the beginning, so as (if possible) to create an interest for the symbolism of chemistry in the purely educational world. I hope, at some future time, to carry the matter out, and to clothe the mathematical conceptions which are necessary to fully appreciate your views with a few simple illustrations adapted as much as possible to the popular mind, or to any mind that has a desire to be acquainted with the progress of science.

My personal experience in relation to the reception of your system by chemists is that they have an incorrect and unfortunate tendency to translate its symbols into those that express the results of the atomic theory, and that in consequence they shut themselves out from the true perception of its beauties.

I also send you a little book that aims at making the entrance into chemical science more attractive than it usually is, by treating the subject in a simple and orderly manner.[116] I hope to get a good adoption of this book, which I am told is a step in the right direction.

I am Sir,

Yours very truly,

W. H. Walenn

Sir B. C. Brodie

In his article, published in a rare journal,[117] Walenn briefly reviewed the introduction of the Daltonian and Berzelian nomenclature and examined its faults in the light of modern chemistry. Brodie's new system was 'the most remarkable chemical theory that has ever been put before the world, characterized alike by the ingenuity and simplicity of its conceptions.' Chemists who attempted to translate Brodie's symbols back into traditional notation transgressed

'the laws of logic and exact reasoning, and introduce[d] the atomic theory into a theory that does not need such intermediate and encumbering ideas, but which seeks to effect for chemistry the same beneficial results that have accrued to mechanics and other sciences from the direct application of mathematical and logical reasoning thereto—so that the results obtained have simply reference to the experiments

K

tried, and to the reasoning upon them in a simple, but strictly exact manner.'

In Brodie's system, experimental results were summarized 'in literal terms that cannot be confounded with anything that has atoms for its basis, thereby allowing of the contemporaneous existence of the two systems, until one (and we must say that at present we think the atomic) dies a natural death.'

Brodie would surely have been pleased with Walenn's understanding and praise. However, like other contemporary chemists, Walenn had been most impressed by the implication which the system had of a reduction in the number of elements.

'Can the symbols of these bodies (nitrogen and chlorine) be interpreted, as showing that, in some condition, (abnormal on this planet, or attainable, but yet undiscovered,) they are resolved into simpler parts, one of which is hydrogen? Or, on the other hand, does interpretation fail here, in regard to the matter under consideration, as it does in the case of "impossible quantities" or the square roots of negative quantities, when the question implies only one plane of reference?'

Nitrogen was as inert as any compound; it was neither magnetic nor diamagnetic; and it possessed a complex spectrum like a compound body. Chlorine had been once reasonably believed compound.

'These facts taken in connection with the "occlusion" of hydrogen to a surprising extent by palladium, meteoric iron, and other bodies, that has been recently pointed out by Dr Graham, already form a nucleus of thought, that, if carried out by the powerful electric and other decomposing forces, at present at our command, may prove the truth of the external and objective interpretation of these symbols, and unfold their value in a practical manner.'

Although Brodie had been guilty of such speculation, we may judge from the following letter that he felt that Walenn's tone had been a little too positive.

28. FROM W. H. WALENN[115]   LONDON 1867

19 Talbot Road,
Tufnell Park West, N.
Dec. 2nd, 1867

Sir,

I have to acknowledge the receipt of your note with much pleasure. I am sorry that I should have introduced a speculative idea respecting the nature of the operations which form the basis of your Calculus.

As I am fond of having all points correct, I think of sending a note, of which a copy is enclosed, to the Editor of the journal // for publication // setting the matter right. I shall not send it, however, until I know your pleasure.

Your approval of and kind suggestion respecting my book is very acceptable to me; it accords entirely with that given by Dr W. A. Miller, and by Prof. Wheatstone.[118] The latter also suggested a change of title, which will be made a point of serious consideration.

I am Sir,

Yours very truly,

W. H. Walenn

Sir B. C. Brodie

(Copy)   19 Talbot Road
Tufnell Park West
London N.
Dec. 1867

Dear Sir,

It is right to observe, respecting my article 'On Chemical Notation,' in no. 3 of the 'Quarterly Journal of Education,' that the kind of operation used by Sir B. C. Brodie to construct his symbols upon is an abstract operation, and (in relation to chemistry) stands somewhat upon the same basis as an unknown quantity, or as a symbol whose interpretation is not yet fully arrived at does, in ordinary mathematics.

Sir Benjamin Brodie has kindly noticed this fact to me, and I feel convinced (after due consideration) that any speculative statement of the nature of the operation, such as that made by me, is forestalling the result of an exact mental process; for the kind of operation can only be truly pointed out by the laws of the interpretation of symbols.

Yours truly,

W. H. Walenn

T. J. Allman Esqre.

Brodie was evidently not completely satisfied by this proposal for he suggested an addition to Walenn's first paragraph, which then read:

> 'It is right to observe, respecting my article . . . or as a symbol whose interpretation is not yet fully arrived at does, in ordinary mathematics, it being possible to investigate the relation which exists between the various chemical operations by which the units of ponderable matter are severally constructed, without defining the nature of a chemical operation further than by its result, which is 'weight' or matter itself.'[119]

The account of Brodie's lecture to the Chemical Society which had been published in *Chemical News*[120] suffered from several errors. Brodie, who later published a corrected version of the lecture,[121] had evidently mentioned some of the less obvious errors to Walenn.

29 FROM W. H. WALENN[115]   LONDON 1867

19 Talbot Road,
Tufnell Park West
London N,
Dec. 5th 1867

Dear Sir,

By this post I send a letter to the Editor of the 'Quarterly Journal of Education' in accordance with the opinion you have expressed, and with the addition that you have kindly suggested, which to my mind completes the necessary correction.

I have the copy of the Chemical News that contains the report of your lecture but *not* the corrected copy.

I do not pretend to have read over this report critically, but, having been present at the lecture, I noticed a discrepancy between the lucid illustration you gave of the geometrical construction of the formula $a + b$, and the drawings or diagrams given in the report. No idea of a parallelogram is present there, but the construction of the symbol makes it absolutely necessary, for $a + b$ is the diagonal of the parallelogram of which a and b are respectively the sides.

In my study of mathematics I have met with this method of constructing $a + b$, and I believe it forms the commencement of a work on algebraical geometry, but cannot at the present moment call to mind the author's name.[122]

To a person thoroughly versed in mathematical physics, the same idea might be illustrated by the parallelogram of forces, $a + b$ being the resultant of the conjoint action of the forces a and b.[123]

I do not know whether other errors are not in the report, but shall be glad to have a true record from yourself.

Very truly yours,

W. H. Walenn

Sir B. C. Brodie

P.S. I send herewith No. 1 of the Educational Journal already mentioned, as it contains my article on 'Teaching chemistry in schools.'[124]

W.H.W.

Another positivist participant in the Williamson debate of 1869 and its aftermath had been the brilliant organic chemist, Charles Alder Wright.[125] His ideas, which were very similar, and therefore attractive to Brodie, made him the centre of another controversy over atomism when he read a paper to the Chemical Society in February 1872.[126]

30. FROM C. R. A. WRIGHT[127]   LONDON 1872

Chemical Laboratory
St. Mary's Hospital,
Paddington. W.
Febr. 26th 1872

Dear Sir,

I thank you much for the copy of your Memoir of the Calculus of Chemical Operations, & also for the kind way in which you speak of my recent paper, or rather the additions to the brief report of it that appeared in the Chemical News.

Your profound writings were not unknown to me before; indeed I had the pleasure of being present at the lecture on the subject that you gave to the Chemical Society some few years ago; & it is in part the consideration of your ideas on the one hand & those of the Atomists on the other, that has led me to my present notions on the subject.

You say (p. 856) after quoting Gerhardt, 'how unreasonable is it to attempt the expression of a formula by symbols which not only permit but even compel us to regard it from the atomic point of view. We cannot adopt the atomic symbol & at the same time declare ourselves free from the atomic doctrines.'

I have not been able to agree with you as to the *compulsion*, nor as to the necessity of involving the atomic hypothesis in the symbols ordinarily (though not necessarily, as I think) employed in connection with that hypothesis. I wrote the paper referred to with the endeavour to show firstly that the ordinary symbolic expressions merely represent ascertained facts & refer to certain well established generalisations; secondly that the atomic hypothesis, while readily accounting for some of these facts, & being in harmony with certain of these generalizations, is yet insufficient with respect to several facts & generalisations.

Your elaborate system, & the ordinary one as I have endeavoured to define it, are therefore alike in this respect, that each is a representative solely of facts apart from any hypothesis; but, while admitting the superior exactitude of your system, I would submit that the comparative simplicity of the ordinary system is a point in its favour so far as teaching is concerned;[128]

&, (symbols being viewed as means of colligating many facts & expressing them in brief) that it had some little advantages over yours as a means of serving as a "memoria technica" of facts. For example one sees from the formula H.OH, Na.OH not merely the quantitative gravimetric or volumetric composition of these bodies, but also a reference to the fact of their mutual convertibility by suitable reactions, & to the fact that *half* only of the hydrogen in water is eliminated by the action of sodium. I do not see that the symbol $a\chi$ expressed this latter fact so clearly. Again the action of chlorine on marsh gas producing successively C_3HCl CH_2Cl_2 $CHCl_3$ CCl_4 is referred to by the symbol CH_4 as well as its quantitative composition; but I do not see that the symbols $a^2\kappa$ $a^2\chi\kappa$ $a^2\chi^2\kappa$ $a^2\chi^3\kappa$ $a^2\chi^4\kappa$ express this so clearly; & again numerous reactions of acetic acid are referred to by the 'dissected formula' $CH_3 \cdot CO \cdot OH$, but I do not see how the many decompositions called to mind by this symbol are denoted by $a^2\kappa^2\xi^2$.

You will not, I am sure, be offended by my mentioning thus some points that have occurred to me, which seem to me somewhat to diminish the *practical* value of your system.

I regret to learn from the newspapers that your health compels you to give up your chair.[129] I presume from what I hear, that Mr Vernon Harcourt will be your successor, & that there will be probably no open competition for the appointment.

I am yours faithfully

Chas. R. A. Wright

31. FROM C. R. A. WRIGHT[127]   LONDON 1872

Chemical Laboratory
St. Mary's Hospital,
Paddington. W.
March 7th 1872

Dear Sir,

I thank you for the information about the Wayneflete [*sic*] Professorship of Chemistry.

It seems to me that the terms of the Atomic Theory, e.g. Atom, are used in two senses by chemists; one as a material something, possessed of dimensions in space mass & time, the other as a simple number or ratio not possessed of such dimensions: so that when Dr Williamson says that 'the so called law of multiple proportions has no existence apart from the atomic theory' (Chem Soc J.)[130] he is using the term Atom in the latter, & not in the Daltonian sense to which you restrict it, & with truth as it seems to me. Certainly the words cannot be always employed in the same sense, or the contradictory statements one meets with in books could not be made.

It seems to me that the formula H_2O & the pictorial symbol ●—O—● represent two different sets of ideas: the former just the facts that 2 vols of steam contain 2 of hydrogen & 1 of oxygen: that 9 parts by weight yield 8 of oxygen and one of hydrogen: & that the chemical reactions of water are such as to produce compounds whose formulae are related to that of water, e.g. NaHO: the latter represents the theory of the existence of finite indivisible portions of matter, & a notion as to this mode of union or connection.

I am yours faithfully,

Chas. R. A. Wright

Sir Benjamin Brodie

The final letter in the collection concerns the mathematician William Clifford's efforts to develop a chemical algebra based upon *atomic* reasoning. In part II of his Calculus (1877), Brodie noted that there could only be a or a^2 systems, and a more general indeterminate system which included both of them, and from which they could be derived. Thus if,

Hydrogen $= a'\omega'^2$ Chlorine $= a'\chi'^2$

Hydrogen chloride $= a'\chi'\omega'$

If we put $\omega' = 1$, we obtain the a system.

If we put $a' = 1$, we obtain the a^2 system.

Brodie, who claimed that a determinate system was better than an indeterminate one, had had the latter pointed out to him by Stokes in 1866, and he noticed that Crum Brown had referred to it in 1867 long before Clifford discussed it before the Belfast meeting of the British Association[131] in 1874. Perhaps this is why Clifford did not publish his notation. However, after hearing Clifford at Belfast, Sylvester was inspired to develop his Chemical Algebra.[132] Odling was in the Chair at the Chemical Society when Clifford repeated his ideas,[133] and he subsequently reported the affair to Brodie.

32. FROM W. ODLING   OXFORD 1874[134]

15 Norham Gardens,
Oxford
November 22nd [1874]

My dear Sir Benjamin,

I did not hear Clifford's paper at Belfast or see the account of it in 'Nature' so that what he gave us at the 'Chemical' on Thursday last, came upon me quite unprepared, and I make you the best report I can.

Taking volumes or molecules he starts from such general equations as the following—applicable of course to different classes of reactions.

$$1. \quad a + \ b = 2c$$
$$2. \quad a + 2b = 2c$$
$$3. \quad a + 3b = 2c$$

Considering that in all these equations the sum and difference of any matter the two reagents have in common must be dipartite and what each has of different matter must also be dipartite he resolves the first equation $a + b = 2c$ into

$$xyy + xzz = 2xyz$$

where x represents what matter, more or less, simple or compound, the reagents have in common, y and z what each has of different matter. Supposing $x = 0$ or that there is no common constituent, the equation becomes

$$yy + zz = 2yz$$

Supposing $z = 0$ or that b is included in a, the equation becomes

$$xyy + x = 2xy$$

the former corresponding to the common expression

$$Cl_2 + H_2 = 2ClH$$

the latter to your expression

$$a\chi^2 + a = 2a\chi$$

While then, the common expression, and your expression could both be true Clifford claims for his expression that it is in any case necessarily true. Similarly he resolves the 2nd & 3rd equations thus:

$$a + 2b = 2c \text{ into}$$
$$xxyy + 2xz = 2xxyy$$

and

$$a + 3b = 2c \text{ into}$$
$$xyy + 3xzz = 2xxyzzz$$

He then argued in disproof of your position as to a being indistributable, [based] relying in fact on the relationship of nitric oxide to its constituents

$$av^2 + \xi^2 = 2\left(\tfrac{1}{2}a \cdot v\xi\right)$$

but as I am inable to reproduce his mode of argument I have written to him for a line of explanation.

He began by asserting dogmatically the atomic constitution of matter to be no longer hypothetical or matter for argument, but matter of fact.[135] i.e. the considered expression of observed fact as that a gas was demonstrably constructed of particles at remote distances from one another—though this seemed to me beside the question of equations.

You will be interested in learning that Clerk Maxwell has undertaken to give a lecture at the Chemical Society on the Mechanical Theory of Gases in its relations to Chemical doctrine.[136]

Believe me
Yours very truly
W. Odling

APPENDIX

Comte, Williamson and Brodie

by

W. H. BROCK

IT has been suggested that a significant source of atomic scepticism in the mid-nineteenth century was the Positivism of the French scholar August Comte, since this included the thesis that knowledge only consists in the description of the coexistence and succession of phenomena.[1] Positivism, said Comte, was the final stage of a long historical inquiry preceded by periods of theology and metaphysics. All that we know, or can know of reality is only to be gleaned from what we can observe, or legitimately deduce from observation. Hence, all that we can claim to know should be capable of empirical verification. In his *System of Positive Philosophy* (1838),[2] in which the chemistry was extremely dated, Comte proposed that the task of the chemist was a purely phenomenal one, and he argued firmly against attempts to mathematize chemistry, or to link it with physics.

> 'Every attempt to refer chemical questions to mathematical doctrines must be considered, now as always, profoundly irrational, as being contrary to the nature of the phenomena. . . . It would occasion vast and rapid retrogradation, by substituting vague conceptions for positive ideas, and an easy algebraic verbiage for a laborious investigation of facts.'[3]

It is difficult to believe that Comte would have approved of Brodie's Calculus and its uncompromising use of mathematics; nor were their attitudes towards atomism very similar.[4]

The task of science was not just to collect facts, Comte wrote, but to establish laws by deliberate acts of rational thought. This involved setting up hypotheses which had 'the character of simple anticipation[s] of what we might know at once, by experiment and reasoning, if the circumstances of the problem had been more favourable than they are.'[5] But hypotheses which entailed anything altogether inaccessible to observation and to reason were misleading, dangerous, and unscientific (*i.e.*, metaphysical and unpositive). Thus, Proutian speculations which aimed to reduce the number of empirically defined elements were obscure and dubious 'since we then pronounce upon the mode of agglomeration of elementary particles, which is a thing radically inaccessible to us.'[6] Nevertheless, Comte wrote favourably of Dalton's 'great atomic theory' as 'a happy generalization' and a useful logical artifice.[7] It seems clear that Comte understood by Dalton's atomic theory nothing more than the laws of definite and multiple proportions. The atoms, or particles, were themselves inextricable, and Wollaston's transformation to chemical equivalents, although only an artifice of language, did ensure a more positive character to chemistry since it restrained the tyro from wandering after inaccessible objects. It would appear therefore that Comte, whose grasp of chemistry was very limited, wrote within the textbook tradition.

It is doubtful whether it can be claimed that Comte had any direct influence on the outspoken sceptics of atomism during the 1860s. Huxley, always a useful mouthpiece for judging the climate of opinion, in his famous denunciation of Comte in 1869, denied that the French savant had anything useful to say to scientists; and what he had said of value had been already stated by David Hume in the previous century.[8] The only British chemist, as far as I know, who mentioned Comte by name during the controversies over atomism is the rather obscure pupil and collaborator of A. W. Hofmann, F. O. Ward, who noted in a letter to *Chemical News* that many of the scientific objections to the atomic theory had been proposed already by philosophers like Comte.[9] In France, of course, there were three noted chemists who adopted Positivism as a philosophy: Marcellin Berthelot, Alfred Naquet and Grégoire Wyrouboff. However, two of these, Naquet and Wyrouboff, were conventionalists in their attitude towards atomism and, indeed, like Frankland, Naquet was one of the principal exponents of the new structural chemistry.[10] The ideas of Laurent and Gerhardt on chemical formulae were positivistic, but references to Comte have not been found in their work.[11] Positivism was never the exclusive intellectual property of Comte, nor was it peculiar to the chemists of the period discussed in this book for, despite their statements to the contrary, physicists were equally positivistic towards their theories of light and electricity.

However, personal contact is known to have existed between Comte and Alexander Williamson.

Born of Scottish parents in London, 1824, Williamson was racked by physical disabilities from childhood: a useless stiff left arm, blindness in one eye, and short-sightedness in the other. But apparently he was able somehow to overcome these deficiencies in the laboratory. His father, who worked for the East India Company, was a friend of the utilitarian philosopher and economist James Mill, and he joined with those pioneers who founded the University of London in 1826.[12] When Williamson's father retired in 1839, the family removed to the continent where, in 1841, Williamson entered the Medical Faculty of the University of Heidelberg—only to be soon attracted into the neighbouring field of Chemistry where Gmelin was professor. From Heidelberg, like many another aspiring British chemist, Williamson joined Liebig at Giessen where he spent three valuable years, performed three serious pieces of research, had his work published, and was rewarded by his doctorate in 1845.

Apparently of independent means, Williamson settled in Paris where he set up his own private research laboratory and formed important friendships with the brilliant school of French chemists, Laurent, Gerhardt, Wurtz and Dumas. Of great interest is his contact with Comte with whom he took lessons in higher mathematics upon the recommendation of James and John Stuart Mill. At first the latter tried to get Comte to take Williamson *en pension*,[13] but Comte, who had had a disastrous experience of this system, and despite his financial difficulties, would only agree to 'de hautes leçons particulières, scientifiques ou philosophiques.'[14] Nevertheless, the relationship between Comte and Williamson seems to have been quite intimate.

Williamson was highly pleased by Comte and he wrote home enthusiastically to his father of Comte's 'superior powers.'[15] The French savant was equally pleased with Williamson, and Comte evidently hoped that he would become one of his first English disciples, and proselytize on his return to England. It would be very surprising, therefore, if Williamson had not been influenced by his contact with the source of French Positivism. Some of these philosophical influences can be educed from most of Williamson's subsequent papers, though perhaps not to such a degree as might have been expected. For example, Comte had taught in his *Cours* that catalysis was a metaphysical fancy which was out of place in the positive stage of chemistry,[16] and in his famous theory of etherification, the notion of the 'catalytic force' which had been introduced into chemistry by Berzelius, was completely banished by Williamson.[17] In an obituary notice, Williamson's pupil and colleague, George Carey Foster, noticed that the rambling address which Williamson gave to the British Association at Bradford in 1873 was especially rich in Comtean undertones.[18] For instance, to paraphrase some of Williamson's remarks which echo those of Comte: If chemistry is to be a science it must have a theoretical level of connecting ideas, otherwise it is just a heap of facts. The chemist must cultivate memory and accuracy. He must search for truth, 'for in proportion as our ideas are true do they give us the power of directing these processes.' We penetrate to the truth (*i.e.*, to Comte's positive stage) by using models in which we try to form in our minds:

> 'a distinct image of a thing capable of producing these various appearances; and when we have succeeded in doing so, we look at it from the various points of view from which the natural object had been examined, and find that the ideas so obtained meet at the central image.'[19]

Science develops by a series of compromises until this positive stage is reached. 'A science is but a body of ideas respecting the order of nature.'[20] Theories guide us in arranging facts;[21] chemical theories are merely condensed statements of fact, or mere symbols.[22]

Williamson's inaugural lecture on his appointment to the Chair of Chemistry at University College in 1850 was regarded by Comte as the initial move in a new missionary campaign to convert the English to his Positive System which had then entered its final social and spiritual phase.[23] Williamson's lecture, *The Development of Difference the Basis of Unity*, is an incredibly dull sociological tract; yet when Comte received a printed copy, he discussed it with his French disciples and sent back their collective criticisms to Williamson together with general advice on the best way to propagate the Positivist cause.[24] However, Williamson was to prove a disappointing advocate; once in his Professorial Chair, and engaged in the training of students, he appears to have lost all interest in the propagation of Positivism.[25] He never referred to Comte by name in any of his scientific or other writings even though privately he maintained his friendship with Comte and the other Positivists. Like Benjamin Brodie, Williamson was a resolute agnostic, and the aspirations and semi-religious ritual of the French and English Religion of Humanity can have appealed as little to him as it did to Huxley.[26]

The careers of Brodie and his friend Williamson show some interesting parallels. After very different kinds of education both men came to study chemistry with Liebig at Giessen; unusually for chemists both men had studied mathematics; both men set up private research laboratories before obtaining university appointments; both came to the attention of the scientific community through work in organic chemistry which was published in the early stages of their careers; both were agnostics; both were interested in the reform of scientific education; and both men appeared to retire early from active scientific research in order to pursue their visionary ambitions: Williamson the fruitless pursuit of private industrial chemistry, and Brodie the idealism of his Chemical Calculus.[27] Even more than Williamson, Brodie allowed philosophical influences to guide the direction and interpretation of his research. By 1864 he had decided that the object of science was to *describe* and classify, and not to explain. This attitude was much more than the conventional Baconism of the textbook tradition that facts must be separated from hypotheses; it was rather the determined and rigorous positivism of Hume. For Brodie, unlike Williamson, and no doubt influenced by Gerhardt, the chemist could only hope to examine the properties and behaviour of substances and never understand what they really were. Unfortunately, he thought, chemistry had gone off the rails of this philosophy and instead of representing phenomena by symbols which corresponded with observable facts, it had erected confusing models like the atomic theory between the facts and their description. In place of such a 'thoroughly materialistic bit of joiner's work'[28] Brodie offered

'a system of marks and combinations of letters, which, however, we are not free to arrange and to interprete according to the dictates of caprice, but of which each has a specific meaning assigned to it in the Calculus, from which the laws are deduced according to which it is permitted to operate upon it.'[29]

Unlike the atomic theory, which postulated microscopic entities that seemed to be subject to no fixed rules, Brodie's system was firmly based on fact, 'for it presents only two objects to our consideration, the symbol and the thing signified by the symbol, the object of thought and the object of sense.'[29]

So Williamson and Brodie agreed with the positivistic tradition that metaphysical, or hypothetical, entities had to be cleared away from chemistry, and that the laws and propositions of this science had to be verified by observations. Yet whereas for Brodie *atoms* were metaphysical structures, for Williamson they were positive entities whose existence was experimentally justified. Moreover, whereas for Brodie, chemical symbols, in Gerhardt's words, 'ne sont pas destinées á représenter l'arrangement des atomes, mais elles ont pour but de rendre évidentes, de la manière la plus simple et la plus exacte, les relations qui rattachent les corps entre eux sous le rapport des transformations,'[30] for Williamson (even though he had studied with Gerhardt) they were models 'capable of producing the various appearances,' and could be used 'as an actual image of what we rationally suppose to be the arrangement of constituent atoms in a compound.'[31]

In view of Williamson's belief in the truth of the atomic theory, he can hardly be labelled a philosophical positivist even though he had studied Positivism with Comte. Williamson's attitude towards theoretical entities was not the same as Comte's, nor was it anything like Brodie's. It can be said that while Williamson, like Huxley, accepted the originality of Comte's sociology, and unlike Huxley probably accepted Comte's analysis of the development and classification of the sciences, he did not find this incompatible with atomism. In fact his attitude towards atomism is best described as pragmatic, and his intellectual model as Lavoisier, and not Comte. So that, whereas for Comte and the later phenomenologists like Mach, atoms were only convenient pictures,[32] for Williamson they had a real existence and properties that were capable of serious experimental study. In this respect they were similar to chemical elements, and he advised that chemists should treat them empirically, and at the same time adopt a positivist attitude towards the structure of the atom, just as Lavoisier had recommended with the element. Brodie, on the other hand, was unable to go as far as this, and he sincerely believed that chemists 'went beyond the facts' when they talked of atoms.

In many ways Brodie was the end product of that school of early nineteenth-century chemists who had hoped for a mathematical chemistry; i.e., an axiomatic deductive chemical science. Clearly in satisfying this ambition Brodie owed much to the analysis of logic in terms of algebra which had been made by Boole, and from him Brodie adopted the technical aids of the algebraic laws of distribution, commutation and indices that were to form the basis for his Calculus. In Brodie's case the 'mathematization of chemistry' was bound up with the question of chemical nomenclature which had bothered chemists ever since its introduction by Lavoisier and his colleagues in 1787, and by Berzelius in 1811. If it is true that chemists who felt unable to accept Lavoisier's anti-phlogiston chemistry also felt obliged to reject his nomenclature, it is equally true that anti-atomists were disquietened by Berzelius's atomic nomenclature. Although Berzelius had never attempted a philosophical justification of his symbolism, Lavoisier had tried to justify his own reformation of chemical language by appealing to the *Logique* of l'abbé de Condillac; and it is interesting to note that Brodie did the same. It is clear that Condillac appealed to both Lavoisier and Brodie because he asserted that the words of a language, or the terms of a science, had to be checked to see that they corresponded with real objects or determinate ideas in order to prevent false metaphysical reasoning. 'L'art de raisonner,'

L

wrote Condillac in a famous passage, 'reduit à sa plus grande simplicité, ne peut etre qu'une langue bien faite.'[33] While Lavoisier found in Condillac the justification for ridding chemistry of phlogiston, Brodie found in him the justification and the means to rid chemistry of atoms. Condillac had treated algebra as a language like any other; similarly Brodie treated his own Calculus, or Chemical Algebra, as a language of chemical substances and events.

As it turned out, however, it was Williamson, and not Brodie, who paved the way for the first really successful mathematization of chemical phenomena. For it was Williamson, and not Brodie, who continued the corpuscular tradition of Lavoisier's pupil Berthollet in a search for the mathematical laws of affinity between the particles or atoms of substances, and who reintroduced dynamics into chemistry, thereby opening the way for the mathematical study of equilibria and reaction rates.[34]

NOTES

I. THE ATOMIC DEBATES

Page

1   1 B. Willey, *Nineteenth Century Studies*, London, 1949, p. 154
       and M. Millhauser, *Just Before Darwin*, Middletown, Conn.,
       1959, p. 144.
     2 J. Herschel, *Preliminary Discourse on the Study of Natural
       Philosophy*, London, 1833, p. 299.
2   3 *Ibid.*, p. 305; Herschel later seems to have given the credit
       for the theory to William Higgins, *see* his *Familiar Lectures on
       Scientific Subjects*, London, 1867, p. 453.
     4 *See* L. P. Williams, *Michael Faraday*, London, 1965, esp. pp.
       283-285, for the views of the mathematical physicists at this
       period.
     5 *The Philosophical Magazine*, *40*, 434, 1812. *See* also A. Ure,
       ibid., *57*, 96ff, 1821; *Quarterly Review*, *16*, 47, 1816.
     6 H. Hartley, 'Sir Humphry Davy,' *Proceedings of the Royal
       Society*, *255A*, 167, 1960.
     7 L. L. Whyte (ed.), *Roger Joseph Boscovich*, London, 1961.
3   8 H. Davy, *Syllabus of a Course of Lectures at the Royal Institution*,
       London, 1802, 'Advertisement.' *See* also T. Thomson, *Annals
       of Philosophy*, *4*, 52ff, 1814.
     9 F. C. Gren, *Principles of Modern Chemistry*, 2 vols., London,
       1800, 'translator's note'; R. Heron, *Elements of Chemistry*,
       London, 1800, p. 1.
    10 C. L. Berthollet, *Essay on Chemical Statics*, trans. B. Lambert,
       London, 2 vols., 1804, vol. 1, p. vii.
    11 P. S. Laplace, *System of the World*, trans. J. Pond, London,
       2 vols., 1809, vol. 2, p. 235ff.
    12 Guyton de Morveau, [*Nicholson's*] *Journal of Natural Philo-
       sophy, Science and Arts*, *1*, 110, 1797-8.
4   13 G. Pearson, *ibid.*, *1*, 355, 1797-8; *see* M. P. Crosland, *Histori-
       cal Studies in the Language of Chemistry*, London, 1962, p. 195.
    14 *See* also T. Thomson, *Annals of Philosophy*, *2*, 32, 1813; W.
       Prout, *Annals of Medicine and Surgery*, *1*, 11, 1816.
    15 T. Thomson, *Annals of Philosophy*, *1*, 146, 1813.
    16 J. Davy (ed.), *Collected Works of Sir Humphry Davy, Bart.*,
       London, 9 vols., 1839-40, vol. 8, p. 93.
    17 H. E. Roscoe and A. Harden, *A New View of the Origin of
       Dalton's Atomic Theory*, London, 1896, p. 123; F. Greenaway,
       'The Biographical Approach to John Dalton,' *Memoirs and
       Proceedings of the Manchester Literary and Philosophical Society*,
       100, 1-98, 1958-59.

Page

4   18 Roscoe and Harden, *op. cit.*, p. 100.
5   19 *Ibid.*, p. 159.
    20 *Ibid.*, p. 49.
    21 'Foundations of the Atomic Theory: Comprising Papers and Extracts by John Dalton, William Hyde Wollaston, and Thomas Thomson (1802-1808),' *Alembic Club Reprints*, No. 2, Edinburgh, 1961, p. 35.
    22 *Ibid.*, p. 39.
    23 W. H. Wollaston, *Philosophical Transactions of the Royal Society, 103*, 51-62, 1813.
    24 Wollaston, *Phil. Trans., 104*, 7, 1814.
6   25 'Foundations of the Atomic Theory,' p. 30.
    26 Dalton did try to justify his axioms geometrically. Cf. J. R. Partington, *A History of Chemistry*, London, 1962, vol. 3, p. 807.
    27 *Nicholson's J., 28*, 280-292, 1811.
    28 Wollaston, *Phil. Trans., 112*, 89-98, 1822.
7   29 *Ibid.*, p. 91. Our italics. Wollaston's argument was frequently used by textbook writers, *e.g.*, Edward Turner, *Elements of Chemistry*, 4th ed. London, 1833, p. 197; also *Penny Cyclopaedia*, London, 1835, article on 'atomic theory.'
    30 A very clear exposition of Wollaston's arguments, and of arguments similar in principle due to Michael Faraday (*Phil. Trans., 116*, 484, 1826), may be found in Thomas Thomson, *A System of Chemistry of Inorganic Bodies*, 7th ed., 2 vols., London & Edinburgh, 1831, vol. 1, pp. 4-6.
    31 M. Bunge, *Causality*, Cleveland, 1963, p. 280.
8   32 Roscoe and Harden, *op. cit.*, p. 112. Dalton wrote a paper in *Nicholson's J., 28*, 81ff, 1811, criticizing the way terms like 'atom' and 'particle' were used by his contemporaries; but his own uses are not above criticism.
9   33 *Phil. Mag., 42*, 307, 1813.
    34 W. Whewell, *Philosophy of the Inductive Sciences*, 2nd ed., London, 1847, vol. 1, p. 422.
    35 C. Daubeny, *Introduction to the Atomic Theory*, Oxford, 1831. In the 2nd ed. (Oxford, 1850), Daubeny came out firmly in support for the Prout-Dumas molecular theory. For a review of speculations on the complexity of chemical elements in the nineteenth century, *see* W. V. Farrar, *British Journal for History of Science, 2*, 297-323, 1965.
10 36 Daubeny, *op. cit.*, 1st ed., p. 22.
    37 W. T. Brande, *A Manual of Chemistry*, London, 1819, p. 18. Cf. Turner, *op. cit.*, pp. 195-196; George Fownes, *Manual of Elementary Chemistry*, London, 1844, p. 182; *ibid.*, 6th ed., 1856, p. 210; 11th ed., 1873, p. 241. For reviews of such

Page

textbooks, see *Quarterly Review*, *45*, 392, 1831; *83*, 37, 1848; *96*, 60, 1854.

10 38 M. Donovan, *Treatise on Chemistry* (Lardner's Cabinet Cyclopaedia), 3rd ed., London, 1832, p. 399.

39 G. R. Kirchhoff and R. Bunsen, *Berlin Monatsberichte*, *1859*, pp. 662-665, 783-787; G. Stokes, *Nature*, *13*, 188-189, 1876. Both Kirchhoff and Bunsen were positivists towards atoms.

40 A spectroscopist and Professor of Chemistry at King's College, London. See *Proc. Roy. Soc.*, *19*, xix-xxvi, 1870-71.

41 See *Proc. Roy. Soc.*, *86A*, i-xix, 1912.

42 *Phil. Trans.*, *154*, 413-435, 437-444, 1864.

11 43 This was really an unusual excitation state of oxygen. Cf. F. H. Anstis, *School Science Review*, *45*, 296-301, 1964.

44 J. N. Lockyer, *Phil. Trans.*, *164*, 479-494, 1874; Agnes Clerke, *A Popular History of Astronomy During the Nineteenth Century*, Edinburgh, 1885, pp. 248-253. Professor H. Dingle has kindly pointed out to us that few spectroscopists went so far as Lockyer, and that the latter's relationship with Huggins in particular was 'so strained that they would have felt uncomfortable at agreeing on anything.' (Letter 28/9/65)

45 B. C. Brodie, *Phil. Trans.*, *140*, 759-804, 1850. For a brief biography of Brodie, *see* the introduction to his letters, pp. 91-94.

12 46 *Brit. Ass. Reports*, *33*, 23, 1864.

47 B. C. Brodie, *Phil. Trans.*, *156*, 781-859, 1866.

48 A. W. Williamson was in the Chair. Cf. B. C. Brodie, *Ideal Chemistry*, London, 1880. This is a corrected reprint of the lecture from *Chemical News*, *15*, 295-305, 1867.

49 Brodie, *Ideal Cehmistry*, p. 8.

50 *Ibid.*, p. 13; *Chem. News*, *15*, 296, 1867. *See* editorial comment, *Laboratory*, *1*, 78, 1867. For a defence of 'glyptic formulae,' *see* Fownes, *op. cit.*, 11th ed., p. 244n.

51 For a review of the Calculus and its reception, *see* the essay by D. M. Dallas.

13 52 We owe this formulation to D. M. Dallas.

53 F. Greenaway, *Proceedings of the Royal Institution*, *39*, 189-193, 1962.

54 T. S. Hunt, 'Celestial Chemistry,' *Proceedings of the Philosophical Society of Cambridge*, *4*, 129-139, (1881) 1880-84; reprinted *Chem. News*, *45*, 74, 1882.

55 T. S. Hunt, *Proc. Roy. Institution*, *5*, 178-185, 1866-69; *Chem. News*, *15*, 315-317, 1867.

14 56 *Nature*, *23*, 141-142, 1880-81.

57 T. M. and W. L. Lockyer, with H. Dingle, *Life and Work of Sir Norman Lockyer*, London, 1928, p. 76; letter from

Page

Lockyer to Brodie, 3 May 1874, Brodie papers, Oxford MS Museum *66*. See also *Phil. Trans.*, *164*, 493, 1874. Lockyer appears not to have known of Sterry Hunt's speculations until the latter referred to them in his 'Celestial Chemistry' lecture in 1881. Cf. J. N. Lockyer, *Chemistry of the Sun*, London, 1887, pp. 205-207, where he also gives the incorrect impression that he had not known of Brodie's speculations until about the same time.

14 58 *Life and Work of Sir Norman Lockyer*, pp. 75-76, 102, 107-108; H. A. Jevons, *Letters and Journal of W. Stanley Jevons*, London, 1886, p. 393.

59 J. N. Lockyer, *Proc. Roy. Soc.*, *28*, 157-180, 1878-79; reprinted *Nature*, *19*, 197-201, 225-230, 1878 and *Chem. News*, *39*, 1-5, 11-16, 1879. These experiments were noted by Alfred Naquet who realized they might be evidence for Brodie's system, [*Dr Quesneville's*] *Le Moniteur Scientifique, Journal Des Sciences Pures et Appliquées*, third series, *9*, 390, 1879; reprinted in Brodie's translation, *Phil. Mag.*, series 5, *7*, 427, 1879. A diplomatic report of Lockyer's paper and its reception was published in *The Times*, and reprinted *Nature*, *19*, 157-158, 1878 and *Chem. News*, *38*, 291-292, 1878. See also Crookes's editorial in support of the 'Darwin of the inorganic world,' *Chem. News*, *39*, 65-66, 1879.

60 *Chem. News*, *15*, 295, 1867.

61 *North British Review*, *48*, 211, 1868.

15 62 On vortex atom, *see* R. H. Silliman, *Isis*, *54*, 461-474, 1963.

63 *See* the essay by W. H. Brock, 'Comte, Williamson and Brodie' in the Appendix.

64 For example, the case of W. H. Walenn, *infra*, note 100; cf. also the Wurtz-Berthelot debate, *Nature*, *16*, 293-294, 1877.

65 *Nature*, *6*, 172, 1872. The author was a partisan of atomism.

66 At the Bradford Brit. Ass. meeting in 1873, he stated that the chemical idea of atomism served two good purposes (*Brit. Ass. Reports*, *42*, lxxi, 1873):

'1. It gives a clear and consistent explanation of an immense number of facts discovered by experiment, and enables us to compare them with one another and to classify them. 2. It leads to the anticipation of new facts, by suggesting new compounds which may be made; at the same time it teaches us that no compounds can exist with their constituents in any other than atomic proportions and that experiments which imply the existence of any such compounds are faulty.'

15   67 E. Divers, *Proc. Roy. Soc.*, *78A*, xli, 1907.
     68 One was Edward Frankland, *Lecture Notes for Chemical Students*, London, 1866; *see* p. 2.
16   69 A. W. Williamson, 'On the Atomic Theory,' *Journal of the Chemical Society*, *22*, 328-365, 1869. Extract on pp. 330-331.
     70 *Ibid.*, p. 331.
     71 He had promised to do this in reply to Brodie's anti-atomic stand in 1867, *Chem. News*, *16*, 4, 1867. *See* Brodie letters, no. 17.
     72 In addition, he discussed evidence from atomic heats ('On the Atomic Theory,' p. 357) and structural isomerism (*ibid.*, p. 362).
     73 *Ibid.*, pp. 331-340.
     74 *Ibid.*, p. 334.
17   75 He considered the hydrocarbon $C_{27}H_{56}$. Analysis gave 85·5% C and 14·9% H, which suggested at least three possible formulae, viz.,

$C_{27}H_{56}$	$C_{26}H_{54}$	$C_{27}H_{54}$
C 85·27%	C 85·25%	C 85·71%
H 14·73%	H 14·75%	H 14·29%

Only further analysis of a silver salt, and tests to distinguish paraffin and olefin, could help determine the most probable formula.
     76 Williamson, 'On the Atomic Theory,' p. 336. Our italics.
     77 *Ibid.*, p. 337. Cf. 'no chemical analysis, no matter how refined, will ever be able to show the law of multiple proportions to be wrong,' Pierre Duhem, *Aim and Structure of Physical Theory*, trans. P. P. Wiener, Princeton, N. J., 1954, p. 214.
     78 Williamson, 'On the Atomic Theory,' p. 338.
18   79 *Ibid.*, p. 339.
     80 *Ibid.*, p. 340.
     81 *Ibid.*, p. 337.
19   82 *See* note 71.
     83 Williamson, 'On the Atomic Theory,' p. 365. Our italics. There is more than a hint of Comte in this statement; but compare Lavoisier: discussions on the nature and number of the elements are metaphysical.
         'I shall, therefore, only add upon this subject, that if by the term *elements*, we mean to express those simple and indivisible atoms of which matter is composed, it is extremely probable that we know nothing about them; but if we apply the term *elements* of principles of bodies, to express our ideas of the last point which analysis is capable of reaching, we must admit, as elements, all

Page

those substances into which we are able to reduce bodies by decomposition.'

The elements might really be complex, but since 'they act with regard to us as simple substances . . . we ought never to suppose them compounded *until experiment and observation has proved them to be so.*' From Robert Kerr's trans., *Elements of Chemistry*, Edinburgh, 1790, p. xxiv. In 1867 Williamson's friend Kekulé, in an attack on Brodie, had said: 'The question whether atoms exist or not has but little significance from a chemical point of view: its discussion belongs rather to metaphysics. In chemistry we have only to decide whether the assumption of atoms is an hypothesis adapted to the explanation of chemical phenomena,' *Laboratory*, *1*, 304, 1867, reprinted by Richard Anschütz, *August Kekulé*, Berlin, 1929, vol. 2, pp. 364-369. Finally, Justus Liebig, *Letters on Chemistry*, 4th ed., London, 1859, p. 105, had said that chemists used the term *atom* in a sense precisely analogous to the word *element*.

19 84 Williamson, 'On the Atomic Theory,' p. 343.
85 *Ibid.*, p. 365. Cf. 'Comte, Williamson and Brodie,' Appendix, p. 150.

20 86 *Chem. News*, *19*, 284, 1869.
87 *Chem. News*, *20*, 19, 1869. Mills's paper was unfortunately never printed, nor has the manuscript been preserved; it was undoubtedly more philosophical than chemical.
88 *Ibid.*; as this was the final meeting that session, with four other papers to be read, there would have been no time for discussion.
89 *Chem. News*, *20*, 235-237, 1869. There is a slightly fuller version in *J. Chem. Soc.*, *22*, 433-441, 1869. The original discussion was apparently quite heated, but little of this comes over in the abstract.
90 *Chem. News*, *15*, 295, 1867.
91 The Professor of Chemistry at the Royal College of Science; see *J. Chem. Soc.* (*Trans.*), *87*, 574-590, 1905.
92 Then Professor of Chemistry at the Royal Institution; see *J. Chem. Soc.* (*Trans.*), *119*, 553-564, 1921.
93 A. S. Eve and C. H. Creasey, *Life and Work of John Tyndall*, London, 1945.
94 Obituary, *J. Chem. Soc.* (*Trans.*), *115*, 412-427, 1919.
95 Obituary, *J. Chem. Soc.* (*Trans.*), *119*, 2130, 1921 (a very poor notice).
96 Divers, *op. cit.*, p. xli. Cf. Brodie's lecture of 1867 'will always be memorable in the history of the Society,' *Chem. News*, *15*, 295, 1867.

Page

20 97 *J. Chem. Soc.*, *22*, 440, 1869.

21 98 *Ibid.*, p. 434. Perhaps Williamson could have expressed himself more clearly, as was certainly done by a correspondent to *Chem. News* after the debate had been reported. John Sprague suggested a compromise between the atoms and molecules of the chemist and the continuity revealed by mathematics (*Chem. News*, *20*, 272, 1869):

> 'Both sides are correct. The atoms are the ultimate forms of matter as we know it, in the form of the chemical elements. But no one can affirm, or would think of doing so, that these elements are positively the ultimate forms of matter itself. On the other hand there is a genuine feeling, justified by the remarkable relations between the atomic weights and the properties of the elements, that they are probably compounds of yet simpler forms of matter, though their decomposition may not be possible to man.'

The chemist was entitled to believe that matter is infinitely divisible and nonatomic in ultimate essence, yet appear atomic and indivisible in the forms with which he dealt empirically.

99 *J. Chem. Soc.*, *22*, 435, 1869. Frankland admitted that his attitude towards atomism owed much to Faraday, whose arguments he quoted. At the same time Frankland found chemical difficulties of his own because he pictured the atoms statically. He seems to have ignored the dynamic atomism of Williamson and the molecular physicists.

100 After the discussion, W. H. Walenn, an industrial chemist and disciple of Brodie, wrote that all Williamson's points were debatable. 'When the measure of comparison is weight, it serves no purpose to suppose that matter consists of a collection of individual atoms; for these are not practically weighable, more especially as there is no proof to the eye, the touch, or other sense of the existence of atoms,' *Phil. Mag.*, (4), *39*, 122-126, 1870. *See* also Brodie letters, no. 27-29. Another member of this group was Berthelot, cf. note 64.

101 For example, Wollaston, Prout, and Comte. An outstanding case is Brodie's French translator, Alfred Naquet, who, despite his allegiance to Comtean Positivism, was a rigorous defender of the employment of the atomic theory, *La Philosophie Positive*, *2*, 85-107, 1868.

102 *See* his own *Manual of Chemistry*, London, 1861, Part 1, pp. 2-3. This textbook was especially designed for Brodie's students at Oxford. It is strange that Odling had recently

Page

published a periodic table in which Cannizzaro's atomic weights were crucial, *Quarterly Journal of Science*, *1*, 642, 1864.

22   103   Dalton had said this too; cf Roscoe and Harden, *op. cit.*, p. 159.

104   Divers, *op. cit.*, p. xliii; *Chem. News*, *78*, 286, 1898.

105   His only reference: '[Molecules] are also discovered by an examination of the mechanical properties of gases,' *J. Chem. Soc.*, *22*, 350, 1869.

106   Notice how Brodie's Calculus was ignored. Elsewhere, Mills attacked Miller's argument as a poor excuse for not removing this 'chemical evil'; for 'in the ordinary affairs of life, we acted differently. When anything bad came in our way we endeavoured to remove it without at all considering what we should put in its place. So with the atomic theory,' *Chem. News*, *25*, 67, 1872.

23   107   From a Friday evening discourse printed in J. Tyndall, *Fragments of Science*, 7th ed., London, 1889, p. 108.

108   Foster owed the example to the German thermochemist, Alexander Nauman, *Gundriss der Thermochemie*, Brunswick, 1869, pp. 5-6, which he referred to by its subtitle, *Lehre von den Beziehungen zwischen Warme und Chemischen Erscheinungen* (relations of Heat to Chemistry). Compare Wilhelm Ostwald's phenomenalistic interpretation of compounds, *Fundamental Principles of Chemistry*, trans. Harry W. Morse, London & New York, 1909, pp. 256-257.

24   109   *J. Chem. Soc.*, *22*, 438, 1869. Our italics. This passage is deleted in the *Chem. News* version.

110   *E.g.*, S. T. Coleridge, *The Friend*, 3 vols., London, 1818, vol. 1, p. 155n.

111   T. S. Hunt, *A New Basis for Chemistry, A Chemical Philosophy*, Boston, 1887. All quotations from 2nd revised and augmented ed., Boston, 1888. *See* p. vi. The book was dedicated to J. B. Stallo who was also praised, p. vii.

112   *Ibid.*, p. 15, but first said in 1853 (*American Journal of Science*, *15*, 226-234, 1853). The Dynamic theory of matter had been firmly rejected by Berzelius, *Essai sur la théorie des proportions chimiques*, Paris, 1819, pp. 20-21.

113   Hunt, *A New Basis for Chemistry*, chap. 3.

114   J. B. Dumas, *Annales de chimie*, (3), *55*, 129-210, 1859; 'Faraday Lecture,' *Chem. News*, *20*, 1-7, 1869.

115   Hunt, *A New Basis for Chemistry*, p. 67.

25   116   G. C. Foster, *Chem. News*, *20*, 236, 1869. This phrase did not appear in the *J. Chem. Soc.* version.

117   Despite a 3rd ed. of his book (New York, 1891), a French translation (*Un Système chimique nouveau*, Liège, 1889), and the publication of many articles in *Chem. News*.

Page

25 118 *Phil. Mag.*, (4) *37*, 461-467, 1867; *Phil. Mag.*, (4) *40*, 259-
         263, 1870; *Phil. Mag.*, (4) *42*, 112-129, 1871; *Phil. Mag.*, (4)
         46, 398-405, 1873; *Phil. Mag.*, (5) *1*, 1-16, 1876. As a chemist
         Mills had long been interested in the extension of William-
         son's work on chemical dynamics and equilibria, and he had
         elaborated a theory of fractional precipitation based on the
         law of mass action. According to Morris W. Travers, *A
         Life of Sir William Ramsay*, London, 1956, p. 37, Mills had
         studied in Williamson's laboratory in 1865.

    119 Influenced by periodicity, spectroscopic discoveries, and an
         heritage of Proutian speculations, Mills believed in a uni-
         versal first matter which polymerized to form various ele-
         ments. *See* his 'Pythagorean' papers, *Nature, 23*, 193, 1880-81;
         Phil. Mag., (5) *18*, 393, 1884; *Phil. Mag.*, (5) *21*, 151, 1886.

26 120 *Phil. Mag.*, (4) *42*, 129, 1871. Our paragraph is based on this
         article.

    121 *Chem. News, 33*, 62, 1876.

    122 Divers, *op. cit.*, p. xli, reports that Wright was present. For
         notice of Wright, *see Proc. Roy. Soc.*, *57*, v-vii, 1894.

    123 C. A. Wright, 'On the Relations between the Atomic Hypo-
         thesis and the Condensed Symbolic Expressions of Chemical
         Facts and Changes known as Dissected (Structural)
         Formulae,' *Phil. Mag.*, (4) *43*, 241-264, 1872.

27 124 C. A. Wright, *Chem. News, 25*, 74-75, 1872 (an extension of
         the paper read to the Chemical Society).

    125 Wright, *Phil. Mag.*, (4) *43*, 262, 1872.

    126 *Chem. News, 25*, 67, 1872. This report, and Wright's correc-
         tion (note 124) were read by Brodie. Cf. Brodie letters, no.
         30 and 31.

    127 *Ibid.*, p. 68. Ostwald attempted to do this in his *Fundamental
         Principles*.

    128 *Phil. Mag.*, (4) *43*, 428-433, 1872; *Chem. News, 25*, 249-250,
         1872.

28 129 *Phil. Mag.*, (4) *43*, 503-514, 1872.

    130 *Brit. Ass. Reports, 42*, lxxvi, 1873.

    131 *The Athenaeum*, no. 2395, p. 360, 20 September 1873.

    132 *Athenaeum*, no. 2398, p. 468, 11 October 1873; *Chem. News,
         28*, 230, 1873.

29 133 *Ibid.* Wright practised what he preached at St. Mary's
         Hospital Medical School where he lectured on chemistry.
         For his 2-volume 'calculus' free from hypotheses, see *Phil.
         Mag.*, (4) *43*, 241-257, 1872 and *Chem. News, 28*, 25-27, 1873.

    134 *Athenaeum*, no. 2399, p. 499, 18 October 1873.

    135 A controversy between Wright and the anonymous 'Atom,'
         Chem. News, 28, 281, 295, 317, 1873; *29*, 13, 23, 1874.

Page

29 136 *Nature*, *1*, 44-45, 1869-70. The editor was the reductionist Norman Lockyer.

137 G. M. Fleck, *Journal of the History of Ideas, 24*, 106-114, 1963.

30 138 J. H. Scott, *Journal of Chemical Education, 36*, 64-67, 1959.

139 G. M. Richardson (ed.), *The Foundation of Stereochemistry*, New York, Cincinnati & Chicago, 1901, reprints the relevant papers of van't Hoff, le Bel, and Wislicenus.

140 It should be noted that in 1879 Naquet only asked Brodie for a solution to structural isomerism in terms of the Calculus, *Phil. Mag.*, (5) 7, 418-427, 1879.

141 Divers, *op. cit.*, p. xli. After Williamson's retirement scepticism towards atomism seems to have been strongly influenced by Ostwald at University College, London. *See* M. W. Travers, *op. cit.*, pp. 208 and 251-252. In 1902, in a British Association address, Divers had tried to formulate an atomic theory without hypothesis. His views were strongly attacked by Andrew N. Meldrum in his published thesis, *Avogadro and Dalton*, Edinburgh, 1904.

142 Divers, *op. cit.*, p. xxxiii.

II. THE CHEMICAL CALCULUS OF SIR BENJAMIN BRODIE

Page

31 1 B. C. Brodie, 'The Organic Peroxides Theoretically Considered,' *Journal of the Chemical Society*, *17*, 281-294, 1864; quotation p. 283.

32 2 *British Association Reports, 33*, 23, 1864.

33 3 The scope of the present essay has been necessarily limited by the space at my disposal. The reader who wishes a fuller discussion of the Calculus and of Brodie's other works must refer to my *Chemical Calculus of Sir Benjamin Brodie*, Part 2 Chemistry dissertation, Oxford, 1964.

4 B. C. Brodie, *Philosophical Transactions of the Royal Society of London, 156*, 781-859, 1866.

5 It states that when two volumes of an organic compound are decomposed, the sum of the volumes of the diatomic elements (chlorine, hydrogen, etc.) is divisible by an even number.

6 *Phil. Trans., 156*, 787, 1866.

38 7 In each case, except for arsenic, the decomposition of the hydride is the equation used. For arsenic it is the decomposition of the chloride. The doubled formulae for phosphorus and arsenic are due to the fact that they are tetratomic in the vapour state.

Page

40   8   In the closing section Brodie admits that ammonium chloride is an apparent exception to other compounds in that it does not permit an integral solution. He suggests that this may be because it dissociates, and that similar considerations apply to nitric oxide and dioxide.

     9   *Phil. Trans.*, *156*, 855, 1866.

41   10   *Ibid.*, p. 858.

     11   *Ibid.*, p. 859. *See* Brock and Knight, 'The Atomic Debates,' p. 13.

42   12   *Phil. Trans.*, *167*, 35-116, 1877.

     13   But note also the 'indeterminate' system, *ibid.*, p. 41; and Brodie's letters, no. 32.

43   14   *Phil. Trans.*, *167*, 64, 1877.

45   15   I have used atomic symbols here for the sake of rapid comprehension.

46   16   R. B. Mooney and H. G. Reid, *J. Chem. Soc.*, *1933*, pp. 1315-1318.

47   17   *Phil. Trans.*, *167*, 105, 1877.

     18   *Ibid.*, p. 115. *See* also Brodie letters, no. 7.

48   19   *See* also W. V. Farrar, *Chymia*, *9*, 169-179, 1964.

     20   *See* Brodie letters, no. 2.

     21   B. C. Brodie, *Ideal Chemistry*, London, 1880.

     22   *Chemical News*, *15*, 295, 1867. The lecture was also covered by *Laboratory*, and it is in these two journals that some of the best contemporary discussion is to be found.

49   23   G. Boole, *Mathematical Analysis of Logic*, Cambridge, 1847.

51   24   p. 49.

     25   I feel that this explanation suffers from a certain circularity, as the only way we can find out which elements have this power is by reference to the equations from which their formulae are deduced, and these assume that hydrogen is undistributed. However, on an *ad hoc* basis it is a reasonable explanation.

     26   *Chem. News*, *16*, 2, 1867; *Laboratory*, *1*, 230, 1867 (also prints the discussion).

     27   *See* Brodie letters, no. 1 and 17.

     28   *Phil. Trans.*, *157*, 817, 1866.

53   29   Brodie papers, Oxford MS Museum 67, in the Museum of History of Science at Oxford. These papers include some of Brodie's correspondence and speeches, and many notes and notebooks of material related to the Calculus.

     30   *Laboratory*, *1*, 230, 1867. A copy of Odling's remarks in a neat hand is in the University of Leicester Brodie collection.

54   31   *Ibid.*, p. 198.

Page

54   32 *Ibid.,* p. 206.
      33 *Ibid.,* p. 220
55   34 *See* also Brodie letters, no. 13, 14 and 15.
      35 p. 43.
      36 *Laboratory, 1*, 233, 1867.
      37 *Ibid.,* p. 256.
      38 *See* Brodie letters, no. 6, 7, 8, 9, 10 and 23.
      39 *Laboratory, 1*, 231, 1867.
56   40 *Ibid.,* p. 256. Jevons's stress.
      41 D. F. Gregory, 'On the Real Nature of Symbolic Algebra,'
          Transactions Royal Society of Edinburgh, 14, 208-216, 1840.
          Brodie's footnote is at *Phil. Trans., 156*, 801, 1866.
      42 *Laboratory, 1*, 233, 1867.
      43 *Phil. Trans., 156*, 856, 1866.
57   44 *Laboratory, 1*, 333-336, 1867.
      45 p. 41.
      46 *Laboratory, 1*, 305, 1867.
58   47 *Brit. Ass. Reports, 36*, 29, 1867.
59   48 *Trans. Roy. Soc. Edinburgh, 24*, 691-699, 1867, and Brodie
          letters, no. 23.
      49 Brodie letters, no. 25.
      50 *Philosophical Magazine,* (4), *34*, 129-136, 1867.
61   51 *Phil. Mag.,* (4), *34*, 50-55, 1867.
      52 *Ibid.,* p. 52.
62   53 *Ibid.,* p. 55.
63   54 Brodie papers, Oxford MS Museum 69.
      55 *J. Chem. Soc., 22*, 433-441, 1869; *see* Brock and Knight, 'The
          Atomic Debates.'
      56 R. M. Caven and J. A. Cranston, *Symbols and Formulae in
          Chemistry,* London & Glasgow, 1928, p. 46. It should be noted
          that the abstract of Brodie's remarks makes no mention of
          the Calculus.
      57 *Phil. Trans., 162*, 435, 1872.
64   58 *Proceedings of the Royal Society, 27*, 51-56, 1878; *see* also Brodie
          letters, no. 12.
      59 *See* equation (1) p. 34.
66   60 Brodie papers, Oxford, MS Museum 68.
      61 *J. Chem. Soc.* (*Trans.*), *35*, 673, 1879.
      62 He had stated it in 1864; *see* reference 1.
67   63 *Phil. Mag.,* (5), *7*, 418, 1879.
      64 This point was also made by Wright; *see* Brodie letters, no.
          30.
68   65 J. N. Lockyer, *Proc. Roy. Soc., 28*, 157, 1878-9. *See* Brock and
          Knight, 'The Atomic Debates,' p. 14.
      66 *Phil. Mag.,* (5), *7*, 427, 1879.

Page

68   67 *Ibid.*, p. 429.
69   68 This objection is treated in section III, p. 73.
70   69 J. J. Mulckhuyse in *The Concept and Role of the Model in Mathematics and Natural and Social Sciences*, Dordrecht, Neth., 1961.
      70 p. 55.
      71 Brodie letters, no. 6-10.
      72 A point raised in discussion with Dr J. Crossley of St Catherine's College, Oxford.
71   73 Brodie letters, no. 20.
74   74 *Phil. Trans.*, *156*, 839, 1866.
77   75 *Ibid.*, p. 857.
      76 *Ibid.*, p. 855.
      77 E. Nagel, *The Structure of Science*, London, 1961.
82   78 *See* above, p. 76.
      79 *See* also Appendix, 'Comte, Williamson and Brodie.'
83   80 G. Boole, *Mathematical Analysis of Logic*, p. 13.
      81 *Phil. Trans.*, *156*, 857, 1866.
84   82 *Ibid.*, p. 788.
85   83 Davey and Crum Brown concocted rules by which atomic formulae could be transposed into Brodie's symbols. By doing this they claimed that they had refuted the assertion that the Calculus could not be deduced from the atomic notation. A similar argument was that Brodie had merely substituted Greek symbols for English ones. Both of these objections ignore the fundamental point that the basic assumptions of the Calculus are very different from those of the atomic theory, and that although the written notations have similarities, these do not reflect a similarity of outlook. Indeed it was *because* the operations of the Calculus were so different that Brodie employed Greek symbols.
      84 *Phil. Trans.*, *156*, 856, 1866; Wright thought it was possible, *see* Brodie letters, no. 30.
86   85 *Ibid.*, p. 857.
      86 P. W. Bridgman, *Logic of Modern Physics*, Macmillan paper ed., London, 1960, p. 5.
      87 *See* C. G. Hempel, 'Operationism, Observation and Scientific Terms,' *Philosophy of Science* (ed. by A. Danto and S. Morgenbesser), Meridan paperback, 1960, p. 101.
87   88 *Chem. News*, *15*, 300, 1867.
      79 *Phil. Trans.*, *167*, 116, 1877.
      90 *J. Chem. Soc.*, *17*, 184, 1864.
88   91 *Phil. Trans.*, *156*, 858, 1866.
      92 *See* above pp. 76-82.
90   93 *Logic of Modern Physics*, pp. 62-3.

Page
90 94 *See* article by J. J. C. Smart in A. Flew (ed.), *Logic and Language*, series 2, Oxford, 1961, chap. 12. For the mathematical tradition in chemistry, *see* Brock and Knight, p. 3.

III. SOME CORRESPONDENCE CONNECTED WITH SIR BENJAMIN BRODIE'S CALCULUS OF CHEMICAL OPERATIONS

Page
91 1 Brodie was a friend of all these men. In 1837 he was narrowly beaten in the Newdigate poetry competition by Arthur Stanley, cf. R. F. Prothero (ed.), *Letters and Verses of Arthur Penrhyn Stanley*, London, 1895, p. 28; Brodie's entry, and other examples of his poetry, are in the University of Leicester collection of his papers. *See* also G. Faber, *Jowett*, London, 1957, p. 140.

2 Brodie became prominent in the movement to abolish religious tests for College Fellowships, cf. E. Abbott and L. Campbell, *Life and Letters of Benjamin Jowett*, 2 vols., London, 1897, vol. 1, p. 231; W. R. Ward, *Victorian Oxford*, London, 1965, p. 243. Brodie is quoted as having said 'It is hard for a dog to run with 39 stones around its neck,' J. McCabe (ed.), *A Biographical Dictionary of Modern Rationalists*, London, 1920, p. 113.

92 3 Brodie senior supported the suggestion that Liebig should be elected to the chair of chemistry made vacant by the death of J. F. Daniell at King's College, London. *See* T. Holmes, *Sir Benjamin Brodie*, London, 1898, Appendix G, pp. 232-234.

4 *Philosophical Transactions of the Royal Society*, *138*, 147-170, 1848; *ibid.*, *149*, 91-108, 1849. For a convenient list of Brodie's scientific papers, *see* J. R. Partington, *A History of Chemistry*, vol. 4, London, 1964, pp. 425-427.

5 *Proceedings of the Royal Society*, *86A*, xlvii, 1912.

6 *Phil. Trans.*, *140*, 759-804, 1850; for full discussion, *see* Partington, *op. cit.*, pp. 426-427.

93 7 *Proceedings of the Royal Institution*, *1*, 201, (1852) 1851-54; *ibid.*, *1*, 449, (1854) 1851-54; *Annales de chimie*, *45*, 351-353, 1855; *Phil. Trans.*, *149*, 249-259, 1859.

8 *Chemical News*, *9*, 162, 1864 (an explosion); *Journal of Chemical Society*, *17*, 264, 1864. *See* Dallas's study of Brodie, p. 31.

9 H. M. and K. D. Vernon, *A History of the Oxford Museum*, Oxford, 1909; F. Sherwood Taylor, *Annals of Science*, *8*, 82-112, 1952.

93   10 *Phil. Trans.*, *162*, 435-484, 1872; *ibid.*, *164*, 83-103, 1874.

94   11 *Proc. Roy. Soc.*, *21*, 245-247, 1873.

     12 He is buried in Bletchworth churchyard in Surrey. His wife, Philothea, bore him a son and five daughters. Details of Brodie's life have been taken from Holmes, *op. cit.*, p. 77; R. Hunt, *Dictionary of National Biography*, vol. II, p. 1288 (very poor); and the sources cited by W. V. Farrar, *Chymia*, *9*, 169-170, 1964.

     13 Vernon Harcourt as cited in Vernon, *op. cit.*, p. 61. I am indebted to D. M. Dallas for the remainder of this paragraph.

     14 The Misses P. M. and O. M. Brodie. I am extremely grateful to them for their hospitality and interest; also to the present fourth Baronet, Sir B. C. Brodie, for kindly introducing me to his sisters.

95   15 More likely 1866 than 1867. There is no report of the meeting of the Royal Society on 3 May 1866 when Brodie's paper was read. The Chemical Society, which also met that day, adjourned to hear Brodie's paper, *Chem. News*, *13*, 221, 1866. At the meeting of the Chemical Society, 2 May 1867, which is reported, Williamson made a speech, but did not mention Brodie, *Chem. News*, *15*, 236, 1867.

     16 This refers to a manuscript copy.

     17 Williamson is seen to be already reinterpreting Brodie's symbols atomically; he did this formally in a note to the Royal Society in the following year, *Chem. News*, *16*, 3-4, 1867 and *Laboratory*, *1*, 230-233, 1867. Brodie referred to such mistranslations in *Ideal Chemistry*, London, 1880, p. 62.

96   18 Disuse can be used as a transitive verb.

     19 *British Association Reports*, *33*, 23, 1864.

     20 Stokes was then Secretary of the Royal Society.

     21 *See* Brock and Knight, 'The Atomic Debates.'

     22 Undated, but clearly 1866.

     23 Vernon Harcourt, also Secretary to the Chemical Society.

97   24 Although Stokes spoke at the 1867 meeting, *Chem. News*, *15*, 303, 1867, the Calculus is not mentioned in his writings. Brodie, however, mentions a private suggestion of Stokes's, *Phil. Trans.*, *167*, 42, 1877 and *Ideal Chemistry*, p. 52; cf. my comments on letter 32.

     25 Edward Frankland, *Lecture Notes for Chemical Students*, London, 1866. Odling here refers to Frankland's adoption of Crum Brown's 'glyptic formulae,' cf. Brock and Knight, 'The Atomic Debates,' p. 12.

     26 A. Laurent, trans. W. Odling, *Chemical Method*, Cavendish Society, London, 1855, p. 151: 'I recollect that at one time

M

I admired the penetration of those chemists, who were able to prescribe formulae with numerous parentheses and numerous bracketings. I wondered how they could discover such complicated arrangements. Since then, I have taught a child of eight years old to construct similar formulae, and even to adorn them with one or several copulae, and I am bound to confess that in the fantasies of his constructions, he frequently surpassed the great masters of his art!'

98 27 *Chem. News, 15,* 269, 1867.

28 Undated, but clearly 1867; Odling lectured at the Royal Institution on Graham's diffusion experiments, 25 January 1867, *Proc. Roy. Institution, 5,* 12, 1866-69.

29 Brodie's symbols were independent of caprice since the chemist was 'not free to arrange and to interprete [them] according to the dictates of caprice,' *Phil. Trans., 156,* 855, 1866. In July 1867, Kekulé wrote that Brodie's 'entire speculation is *based on pure caprice*,' *Laboratory, 1,* 305, 1867 (R. Anschütz, *August Kekulé,* Berlin, 1929, vol. 2, pp. 367-368).

99 30 (1814-69) Savilian Professor of Astronomy at Oxford; his principal papers were concerned with mathematical astronomy. His son, William Frederick Donkin, helped Brodie with chemical experiments between 1872 and 1874 (Brodie papers, Oxford MS Museum 66); and with a literature search in connection with the Calculus, *Proc. Roy. Soc., 27,* 53, 1878.

31 (1806-71) Professor of Mathematics at University College, London.

32 (1826-83) Savilian Professor of Geometry at Oxford and a personal friend of Brodie and Nevil Story Maskelyne. Smith believed that the chemical elements were mathematically related, cf. *Collected Works of Henry Smith*, ed. J. W. L. Glaisher, Oxford, 1894, vol. 1, p. xix.

100 33 T. Holmes, *op. cit.*, p. 78; and notebook labelled 'Examples-Calculus,' watermark 1832, Brodie papers, Oxford MS Museum 77.

34 De Morgan Collection, University of London library, bound in with offprint of Brodie's Calculus, Part I, with Author's dedication, Shelf, P (Brodie) fol. I am grateful to the Goldsmiths' Librarian, Mr J. H. P. Pafford, for permission to publish this and letters 8, 9 and 10.

101 35 These brackets have been pencilled in, presumably by Brodie.

36 A pencilled asterisk.

102 37 The whole function has been pencilled in.

Page

102   38   Taylor's theorem was used by Brodie in Part II, *Phil. Trans.* *167*, 112, 1877.

       39   G. Boole, *Mathematical Analysis of Logic*, Cambridge, 1847; A. De Morgan, *Formal Logic*, London, 1847.

103   40   Bartholomew Price (1818-98), Sedleian Professor of Natural Philosophy at Oxford.

104   41   Dalton had died in 1844, cf. H. E. Roscoe, *John Dalton*, London, 1901, p. 148.

       42   Undated and unaddressed, but probably May 1867 from the reference to De Morgan.

105   43   A small edge-tear here; the missing word was clearly '(by.'

106   44   This phrase pencilled in by Donkin.

       45   De Morgan Collection, London.

107   46   This must be a reference to Jevons's treatment of the Calculus as an ordinary algebra, cf. Brodie letters, No. 13-16.

109   47   Brodie's draft, Leicester collection; De Morgan's copy, University of London.

       48   The received version (London) reads: '. . . useless for analytical purposes, for the only processes applicable to such equations are the processes of addition and subtraction, but the very next step, which I am about to take is to effect the transformation of this equation.'

110   49   The London version reads: '. . . The equation is now analytically perfect, that is we may perform upon it [all] every algebraic operation[s] without reserve. It is also interpretable. The main point to be considered (& here I quite agree with you) . . .'

       50   The London version reads: '. . . We hence arrive at a just and exact conception of the nature of the chemical process, which is to be regarded as . . .'

       51   Draft and London version here diverge. The draft is in Brodie's worst hand, and my reading is partly conjectural.

       52   'crab away'—best reading.

111   53   De Morgan Collection, submitted to De Morgan by Brodie as enclosure with letter 9.

112   54   The only mathematicians present were Maxwell and Walenn.

       55   *I.e.*, the day of Brodie's Ideal Chemistry lecture, 6 June.

       56   Presumbly letter 10 of 28 May.

113   57   After the translation of the Calculus into French by the Positivist chemist and atomist Alfred Naquet, it was favourably reviewed by the mathematician C. A. Laisant, *Bulletin des Sciences Mathematiques et Astronomiques*, série 2,

Page

vol. *5*, part I, 1881, pp. 137-149. Brodie's work deserved 'un examen attentif et approfondi.'

113   58 *Proc. Roy. Soc.*, *27*, 54, 1878. *See* Dallas's discussion, p. 64.

59 Brodie papers, Oxford MS Museum 66, undated, but probably 1877. Brodie's paper was received at the Royal Society, 21 November 1877.

60 This point is stressed in the published paper, *Proc. Roy. Soc.*, *27*, 53, 1878.

61 Brodie changed the phrase to 'the paramount influence,' *ibid.*, p. 56.

114   62 *Laboratory, A Weekly Record of Scientific Research*, vol. I, April to September 1867, all published. Brough, who paid contributors, demands investigation, cf. obituary, *J. Chem. Soc.*, *1877*, pp. 774-775. Note also Brough's satirical verse on the Calculus quoted by W. V. Farrar, *Chymia*, *9*, 176, 1964.

63 There is no mention of the Calculus in Harriet Jevons, *Letters and Life of W. Stanley Jevons*, London, 1886.

64 W. S. Jevons, *Pure Logic, or the Logic of Quality apart from Quantity*, London, 1864.

65 This must mean that Jevons had already posted the *Phil. Mag.* manuscript to Brodie before he received the latter's letter and offprint; this would explain the speed with which Donkin and Brodie reacted.

115   66 Undated, but clearly 20-27 May, cf. last note.

117   67 Draft only.

118   68 *Laboratory*, *1*, 198-201, 1867.

69 *Ibid.*, p. 220, cf. Dallas's article, p. 54, for a full discussion.

70 *Ibid.*, p. 233.

71 *Ibid.*, p. 256.

119   72 *Chem. News*, *16*, 3-4, 1867; *Laboratory*, *1*, 230-233, 1867. Only the latter journal prints the discussion which followed. A copy of Odling's remarks in an unknown and neat hand is in the Leicester collection. Cf. Dallas's article, p. 51, and for Williamson's relations with Comte, *see* Appendix.

73 Williamson also referred to it at the Royal Society, *Chem. News*, *16*, 4, 1867.

74 *I.e.*, *for* atoms not against them.

75 My addition, W. H. B.

76 This refers to hydrogen being a not a^2, and chlorine $a\chi^2$; *i.e.*, apparently a compound of hydrogen and the unknown element Y.

120   77 J. A. Wanklyn and R. R. F. Davey, *Phil. Mag.*, (4) *34*, 50-55, 1867. *See* Brodie letters, no. 24.

Page

120 78 For full references, *see* J. R. Partington, *A History of Chemistry*, vol. 4, p. 158.

79 *Brit. Ass. Reports*, *27*, 41-45, 1858; Brodie, *Phil. Trans.*, *156*, 784, 1866.

80 Royal Society Herschel papers, HS4. 293. I am grateful to the Royal Society's librarian, Mr I. Kaye, for permission to reproduce this letter and its companion, no. 21.

121 81 Leicester collection; the Royal Society possesses the draft, HS4. 294, which offers some different readings. I have followed the Leicester version and noted any changes from the draft as deletions.

124 82 Royal Society Herschel papers, HS4. 295.

126 83 Brodie was never elected (personal communication from Herr Dr H. Battré, Deutsche Akademie der Wissenschaften zu Berlin, 10 February 1965). However, Brodie was elected to the Berlin Chemical Society in December 1873 (letter from A. W. Hofmann to Brodie, 17 December 1873, Brodie papers, Oxford MS Museum 66).

127 84 E. K. Kummer (1810-93).

85 Leopold Kronecker (1823-91).

86 Karl Weierstrass (1815-97).

87 Carl Borchardt (1817-80).

88 For Henry Smith, *see* p. 113. Kummer had judged the Steiner prize of the Berlin Academy which Smith won in 1866.

89 H. G. Magnus (1802-70), chemist.

90 Friederich Dorn (1848-1919), physicist and later the discoverer of radium emanation.

91 Gustav Rose (1798-1873), Professor of Mineralogy Berlin.

92 K. F. Rammelsberg (1813-99), chemist.

93 Heinrich Buff (1805-78), physicist.

94 Presumably Emil Heinrich du Bois Raymond who was the Secretary of the Academy; but possibly his brother the mathematician.

95 Hofmann married four times. His second wife, whom he married in 1856, was Rosamund Wilson, who had died in 1860.

96 Hunt stayed with Brodie at Oxford in May, *see* 'The Atomic Debates,' p. 13.

128 97 *Phil. Mag.*, (4) *34*, 129-136, 1867.

98 Black-edged notepaper, cf. *J. Chem. Soc.*, *1923*, p. 3430.

129 99 This was the indeterminate system later exploited by Clifford. *See* Brodie letters, no. 32.

130 100 *Transactions, Royal Society of Edinburgh*, *24*, part III, 691-699, 1867.

Page

130 101 A. Cayley, *Collected Works*, Cambridge, 13 vols., 1889-98, vol. 9, pp. 202, 427, 544.

102 J. S. Griffith, 'Sylvester's Chemico-Algebraic Theory,' *Mathematical Gazette*, *48*, 57-65, 1964. *See* the very interesting articles, *American Journal of Mathematics*, vol. 1, 1878.

103 Brodie was probably convalescing from rheumatic fever at Torquay in Devonshire. Odling seems to imply that Brodie had been shocked by the reception of the Calculus.

131 104 William Francis (1817-1904), editor of the *Philosophical Magazine*.

105 Odling was, among other things, Lecturer in Chemistry at St Bartholomew's Hospital in London, cf. *Chem. News*, *16*, 193-194, 1867.

106 Lyon Playfair (1818-98), then Professor of Chemistry at Edinburgh.

107 *Brit. Ass. Reports*, *36*, 28-31, 1867; *see* Dallas's essay, p. 58.

108 *Ibid.*, pp. 31-32; Dallas, p. 59.

109 *The Dundee Advertiser*, September 1867, p. 91. I am grateful to the Dundee City Librarian, Mr W. S. Taylor, for a xerograph of this discussion which he had the kindness to trace for me.

132 110 Robert Harley (1828-1910), Congregational minister and logician, *see Proc. Roy. Soc.*, *91A*, i-v, 1915.

111 In view of the later reference to Jevons, probably material from *Laboratory*, and perhaps also *Chem. News*.

112 Before the Dundee meeting, Maxwell had asked Kelvin, the President for 1867, 'Have you got anything about Sir B. Brodie or do you leave that to the chemists? They have no right to it.' (Quoted by H. T. Bernstein, *Isis*, *54*, 213, 1963).

113 *British Quarterly Review*, *44*, 141-181, July 1866.

134 114 (1828-96) a pupil of De Morgan, he published several mathematical papers on his theory of 'unitates' in the *Phil. Mag.* and *Quarterly Journal of Education* between 1867 and 1880. He was employed as an electrochemist, obituary, *J. Chem. Soc. (Trans.)*, *1897*, ii, p. 1206. For his positivist attack on atoms, *Phil. Mag.*, (4) *39*, 122-126, 1870; 'The Atomic Debates,' p. 159, Note 100.

115 On mourning paper.

135 116 W. H. Walenn, *Little Experiments for Little Chemists*, London, 1866 (B. M. 8907.a.40).

117 *Quarterly J. Education*, *1*, no. 3, 113-118, 1867, all quotations from pp. 116-118. This issue is only available in the British Museum, PP. 1180.d.

137 118 William Allen Miller (1817-70), Professor of Chemistry at King's College, London; Charles Wheatstone (1802-75),

Page

Professor of Experimental Philosophy at King's College.

138 119 *Quart. J. Education*, *1*, no. 4, 155, 1867.

120 *Chem. News*, *15*, 295-300, 1867.

121 *Ideal Chemistry*, London, 1880.

139 122 Probably A. De Morgan, *Trigonometry and Double Algebra*, London, 1849, which was cited by Brodie in this context, *Ideal Chemistry*, p. 20.

123 Cf. *Ideal Chemistry*, p. 24.

124 *Quart. J. Education*, *1*, no. 1, 13-16, 1867; chemistry 'should be taught according to the latest theoretical views, and with as little as possible reference to theories that rather form a matter of history than of present interest.'

125 *See* 'The Atomic Debates,' p. 26.

126 *Phil. Mag.*, (4) *43*, 241-264, 1872; report only, *Chem. News*, *25*, 67-68, 1872, with elaboration by Wright, *ibid.*, p. 74.

140 127 Brodie papers, Oxford MS Museum 66.

128 Wright laid great stress on teaching, cf. his two-volume system devoid of hypotheses, *Chem. News*, *28*, 25-27, 1873.

141 129 Brodie was succeeded by Odling.

142 130 Wright omitted the reference, *J. Chem. Soc.*, *22*, 339, 1869; *see* 'The Atomic Debates', p. 18.

131 Not printed in the *Brit. Ass. Reports* for 1874; brief report, *Nature*, *10*, 432, 1874. The paper was not reproduced in Clifford's *Mathematical Papers*, ed. R. Tucker, London, 1882, but its material was foreshadowed in a lecture on atoms in 1872, *Lectures and Essays*, ed. L. Stephens and F. Pollock, 2 vols., London, 1879, vol. 1, p. 188.

143 132 *See* my remarks p. 130 and *American J. Maths.*, *1*, 126, 1878.

133 Good report, *Chem. News*, *30*, 244-245, 1874.

134 The dating follows from the preceding discussion.

144 135 Clifford 'had approached the subject from the physical side, and there was no doubt that the kinetic theory of gases, which is merely an expression of facts in another language, amounts to an absolute demonstration of the existence of molecules,' *Chem. News*, *30*, 245, 1874.

136 'On the Dynamical Evidence of the Molecular Constitution of Bodies,' delivered 18 February 1875 with Odling in the Chair, *Nature*, *11*, 357, 374, 1875.

APPENDIX

145 1 W. V. and K. R. Farrar, *Proceedings Chemical Society, 1959*, p. 287; E. F. Caldin, *Structure of Chemistry*, London, 1961, p. 12. It may be remarked that the article by G. Urbain,

Page

'La valeur des idées d'A. Comte sur la chimie,' *Revue de Métaphysique et de Morale*, 27, 151-179, 1920, is not historical.

145   2 Translated by H. Martineau, 2 vols., London, 1853; all citations from the edition in 3 vols., London, 1896.

3 Martineau, vol. 1, p. 289; G. H. Lewis, *Comte's Philosophy of the Sciences*, London, 1853, p. 116.

4 I can find no evidence that Brodie ever read Comte.

146   5 Martineau, vol. 1, p. 242.

6 Lewis, *op. cit.*, p. 340.

7 Martineau, vol. 1, p. 352.

8 T. H. Huxley, *Lay Sermons, Essays and Reviews*, London, 1870. The 6th ed. of 1877 has been used; *see* 'The Scientific Aspects of Positivism,' pp. 147-173.

9 *Chemical News*, 16, 40, 1867. Ward himself was a strict atomist who thought little of Brodie's Calculus, which he completely failed to understand.

10 *See* Naquet's defence that atomism was in accord with the Positive Philosophy, *La Philosophie Positive*, 2, 85-107, 1868. But for its demise this article would have appeared in *Laboratory*; *see* the same, 1, 368, 1867.

11 O. E. Potter, *British Journal Philosophy of Science*, 3, 359, 1952-53 and *Annals of Science*, 9, 271, 1953.

147   12 J. S. Rowe, *Chemical Studies at University College London*, London M.Sc. thesis, 1950, p. 128.

13 *Collected Works of John Stuart Mill*, vol. 13 (Early Letters 1812-48), University of Toronto Press, 1963, p. 668, Mill to Comte 24 June 1845.

14 E. Lerous (ed.), *Lettres d'Auguste Comte A John Stuart Mill (1841-6)*, Paris, 1877, p. 327, Comte to Mill 27 June 1845.

15 Cited by E. Divers, *Proceedings of the Royal Society*, 78A, xxviii, 1907. Unfortunately all Williamson's correspondence has been subsequently destroyed.

148   16 Martineau, vol. 1, p. 325.

17 A. W. Williamson, 'Papers on Etherification and on the Constitution of Salts,' *Alembic Club Reprints*, no. 16, Edinburgh, 1949, pp. 18-19.

18 *Journal Chemical Society (Transactions)*, 1905, i, p. 609; *British Association Reports*, 42, lxx-xci, 1873.

19 *Brit. Ass. Reports*, 42, lxxix, 1873.

20 *Ibid.*, p. lxxxi.

21 *Brit. Ass. Reports*, 50, 569, 1881.

22 *Ibid.*, p. 580.

23 Private communication from J. Harris of Seaford, Sussex. Mr Harris kindly allowed me to read an unpublished biography of Williamson in which he adds that Comte re-

Page

garded Williamson's appointment at University College as a 'véritable événement dans ma vie publique,' and referred to the 'mission anglaise, dont vous [Williamson] êtes le chef naturel.' It must be remembered that at that time Comte's System had not been promulgated in Great Britain by the writings of Harriet Martineau and George Henry Lewes. For orientation, consult W. M. Simon, *European Positivism in the Nineteenth Century*, Ithaca, New York, 1963, p. 89; and for a brief discussion of Williamson's connection with Comte, the same author's 'Comte's English Disciples,' *Victorian Studies*, 8, 162, 1965.

149 24 J. Harris, private communication.

     25 W. M. Simon, who has gone over the ground carefully in the works cited, could find no evidence. However, Williamson appears to have supported some Positivist causes; *e.g.*, see the political pamphlet he wrote with his father-in-law, T. H. Keys, *Invasion Invited by the Defenceless State of England*, 23 pp., London, 1858.

     26 Cf. Huxley's famous denunciation of Positivism as 'Catholicism minus Christianity,' *Lay Sermons*, p. 140; S. Eisen, *Victorian Studies*, 7, 337-358, 1963-64.

     27 Thus Williamson's obituarists were embarrassed by his apparently fruitless life between the ages of 35 and 80; and Brodie was stated by his *D.N.B.* contributor to have produced nothing of importance after 1860. For a brief biography of Brodie, *see* p. 91.

150 28 B. C. Brodie, *Ideal Chemistry*, London, 1880, p. 13; *Chem. News*, *15*, 296, 1867.

     29 *Phil. Trans.*, *156*, 855, 1866.

     30 C. Gerhardt, *Traité de Chimie Organique*, vol. 4, Paris, 1856, p. 566, quoted by Brodie, *Phil. Trans.*, *156*, 856, 1866.

     31 *Chemical Gazette*, *9*, 335, 1851; *Alembic Club Rep.* no. 16, p. 42.

151 32 'and the real mode of agglomeration of elementary particles is, and ever must be, unknown to us, and therefore no proper object of our study,' Martineau, vol. 1, p. 343.

152 33 Georges le Roy (ed.), *Oeuvres de Condillac*, Paris, 1948, vol. 2, p. 409.

     34 F. L. Holmes, 'From Elective Affinities to Chemical Equilibria: Berthollet's Law of Mass Action,' *Chymia*, *8*, 105-145, 1962, esp. pp. 131-132.

THE LOCATION OF BRODIE'S PAPER S

Leicester   The University of Leicester, uncatalogued.

Oxford   The Museum of History of Science, catalogued under MS Museum 66-79, 103.

London   The University of London Library, catalogued under the A. De Morgan Collection.

INDEX

INDEX